Instruction

STAMS® series C

Strategies To Achieve Mathematics Success

Curriculum Associates

ISBN 978-0-7609-6853-6

North Billerica, MA 01862

15 14 13 12 11 10 9 8 7 6 5 4 3

TABLE OF CONTENTS

Lesson 1 PLACE VALUE

PART ONE: Learn About Place Value

How can you find the value of each digit in a number?

Explore

You know how to read whole numbers.

For example, you read 235 as *two hundred thirty-five*.

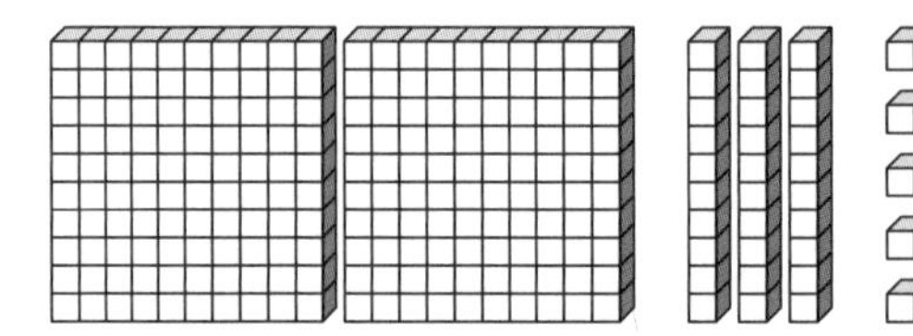

How can **place value** help you understand the value of each **digit** in 235?

Think

A place-value chart tells the value of each digit in a number.

Hundreds	Tens	Ones
2	3	5

Which digit is in the **hundreds place**? 2

Which digit is in the **tens place**? 3

Which digit is in the **ones place**? 5

Connect

The 2 has a value of 2 hundreds, or 200.

The 3 has a value of 3 tens, or 30.

The 5 has a value of 5 ones, or 5.

235 has 2 hundreds, 3 tens, 5 ones

$235 = 200 + 30 + 5$

Let's Talk

Think about showing the number 500 in a place-value chart. What does each zero in the number mean?

Fill in the blanks. Solve the problem.

These blocks show the number 1,208.

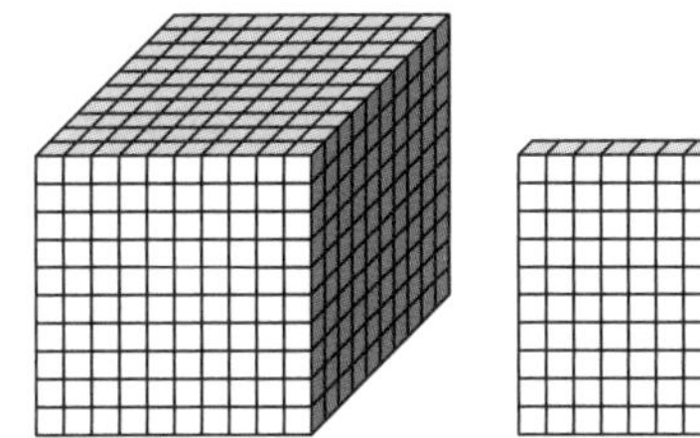
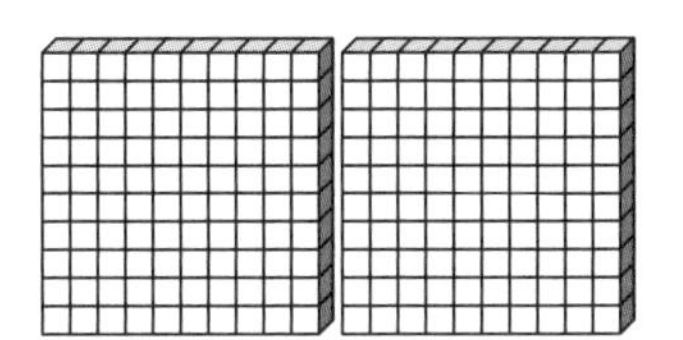

How can you write 1,208 to show the value of each digit?

- How many thousands are shown? _______

  What is the value of the thousands digit? _______

- How many hundreds are shown? _______

  What is the value of the hundreds digit? _______

- How many tens are shown? _______

  What is the value of the tens digit? _______

- How many ones are shown? _______

  What is the value of the ones digit? _______

Solution: 1,208 = 1,000 + 200 + 0 + 8

- One thousand is the same as 10 hundreds.
- One hundred is the same as 10 tens.
- One ten is the same as 10 ones.

Now, use what you know to solve this problem.

1. What is the value of the 6 in 2,460?

Thousands	Hundreds	Tens	Ones
2	4	6	0

Ⓐ 400 Ⓒ 6

Ⓑ 60 Ⓓ 0

How can you use place value to write numbers in different ways?

Explore

You know how to find the values of the digits in a number.

Hundreds	Tens	Ones
7	3	4

734 = 7 hundreds + 3 tens + 4 ones
734 = 700 + 30 + 4

How can you name the values in different ways?

Think

The blocks show 473.

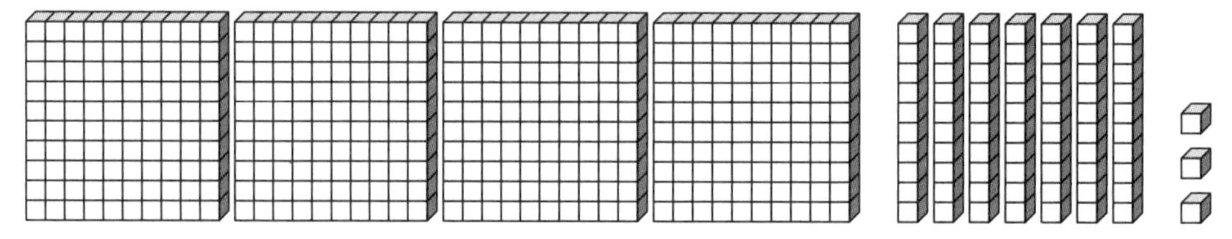

What is the value of the 4? __4__ hundreds

What is the value of the 7? __7__ tens

What is the value of the 3? __3__ ones

473 = __4__ hundreds + __7__ tens + __3__ ones

473 = 400 + 70 + 3

Connect

You can **regroup** 1 hundred as 10 tens.

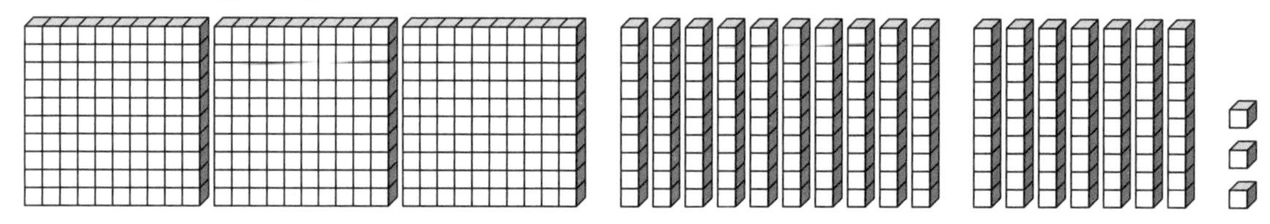

4 hundreds = 3 hundreds and 10 tens

10 tens + 7 tens = 17 tens

473 = 3 hundreds + 17 tens + 3 ones

473 = 300 + 170 + 3

Let's Talk

How can you write 473 using only tens and ones?
Look at the base-ten blocks above to help you.

Fill in the blanks. Solve the problem.

The place-value chart shows the number 3,655.

Thousands	Hundreds	Tens	Ones
3	6	5	5

What is another way to write 3,655 if you regroup 1 hundred as 10 tens?

- How many hundreds are there in 3,655?

  _____ hundreds

- Regroup 1 hundred as 10 tens.

  _____ hundreds = _____ hundreds and _____ tens

- How many tens are there after you regroup 1 hundred?

  _____ tens + _____ tens = _____ tens

Solution: 3,655 = _____ thousands + _____ hundreds + _____ tens + _____ ones

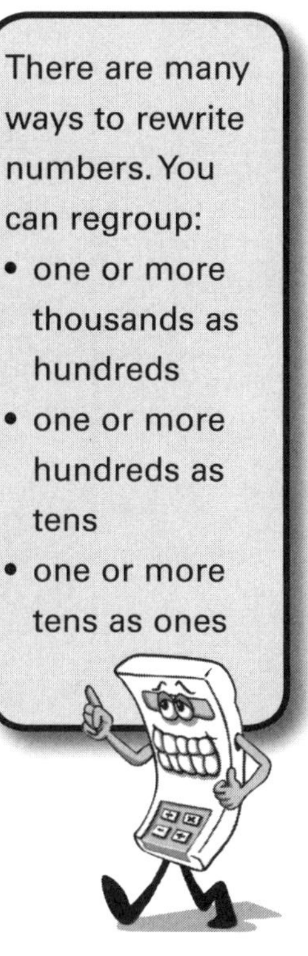

Your Turn **Now, use what you know to solve this problem.**

2. The place-value chart shows 8,024. Regroup 1 thousand as 10 hundreds. Then rewrite the number.

Thousands	Hundreds	Tens	Ones
8	0	2	4

8,024 = _____ thousands + _____ hundreds + _____ tens + _____ ones

Solve the problem. Then read why each answer choice is correct or not correct.

Solve

The blocks show 2,185.

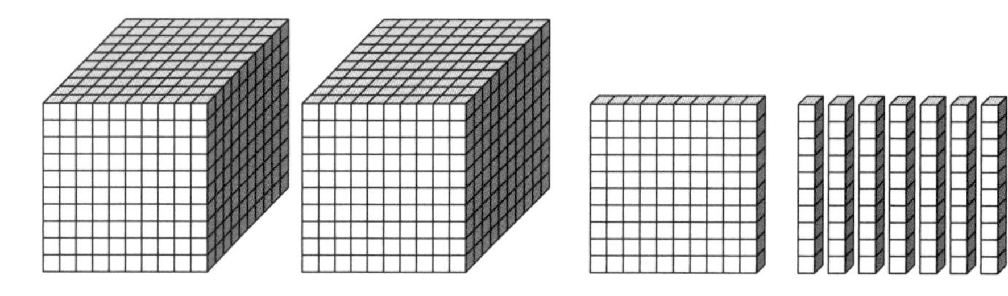

What is the value of the hundreds digit?

Ⓐ 2,000

Ⓑ 1,000

Ⓒ 800

Ⓓ 100

Check

Check to see if you chose the correct answer.

In the number 2,185 the hundreds digit is the 1.

The block shows 1 hundred. The value of 1 is 100.

So, the correct answer is Ⓓ.

Why are the other answer choices not correct?

Ⓐ	2,000	This is the value of the thousands digit.
Ⓑ	1,000	This is the value for 1 thousand, not 1 hundred.
Ⓒ	800	8 is the tens digit, not the hundreds digit.

Your Turn **Solve each problem. Use the hints to avoid mistakes.**

- Find the correct place of the digit. Then figure out the value of the digit.
- Remember that there are 10 ones in 1 ten, 10 tens in 1 hundred, and 10 hundreds in 1 thousand.

3. What is the value of the 9 in 2,495?

Thousands	Hundreds	Tens	Ones
2	4	9	5

Ⓐ 9,000
Ⓑ 900
Ⓒ 90
Ⓓ 9

4. What is the value of the 2 in 1,241?

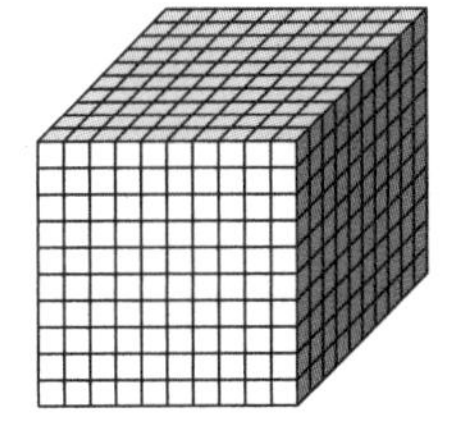
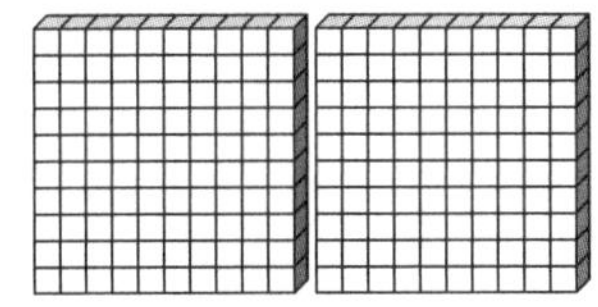
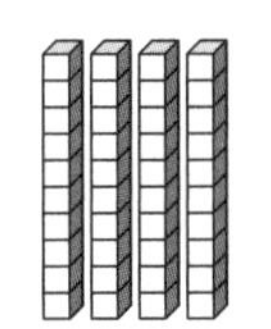

Ⓐ 2
Ⓑ 20
Ⓒ 200
Ⓓ 2,000

5. What number do the blocks show?

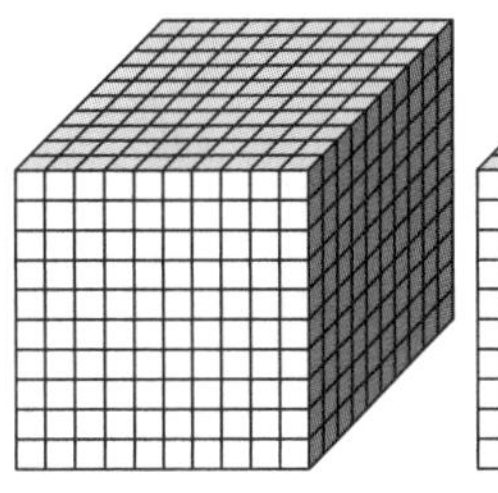
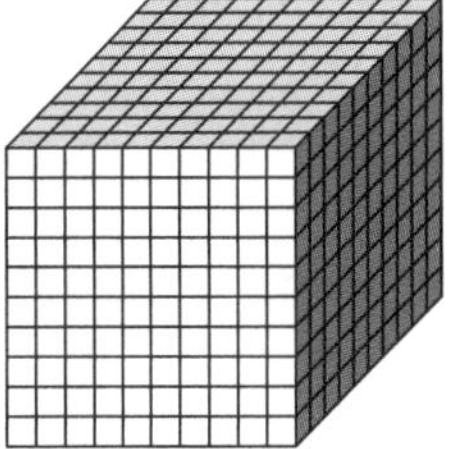
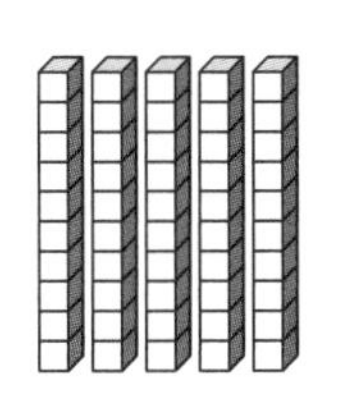

Ⓐ 2,005
Ⓑ 2,051
Ⓒ 2,501
Ⓓ 2,510

6. What is another way to write 348?

Hundreds	Tens	Ones
3	4	8

Ⓐ 2 hundreds + 14 tens + 8 ones
Ⓑ 2 hundreds + 4 tens + 18 ones
Ⓒ 3 hundreds + 3 tens + 8 ones
Ⓓ 3 hundreds + 4 tens + 18 ones

Study the model. It is a good example of a written answer.

Student Model

Show

The place-value chart shows 5,417.

What is another way to write 5,417 if you regroup 1 thousand as 10 hundreds?

Thousands	Hundreds	Tens	Ones
5	4	1	7

Use pictures, words, or numbers to show your work.

5 thousands = 4 thousands + 10 hundreds
10 hundreds + 4 hundreds = 14 hundreds

☑ The student shows each step.

Explain

Solution: __4__ thousands + __14__ hundreds + __1__ ten + __7__ ones

☑ The student correctly answers the question asked.

Explain how you got your answer.

I started with 5 thousands. I regrouped 1 thousand and then had 4 thousands and 10 hundreds. I added the 10 hundreds to the 4 hundreds I already had: 10 hundreds + 4 hundreds = 14 hundreds. The tens place and the ones place did not change.

☑ The student gives important details about how to write the number.

☑ The student uses the math words *regroup, thousands, hundreds, tens place,* and *ones place.*

Your Turn **Solve the problem. Use what you learned from the model.**

7. What is another way to write 2,960 if you regroup 1 hundred as 10 tens?

Thousands	Hundreds	Tens	Ones
2	9	6	0

Use pictures, words, or numbers to show your work.

CHECKLIST

Did you . . .

- ☐ show each step?
- ☐ answer the question asked?
- ☐ give important details?
- ☐ use math words?

Solution: _____ thousands + _____ hundreds + _____ tens + _____ ones

Explain how you got your answer.

____

____

____

____

____

As you solve place-value problems, you may want to
- think about the value of each digit.
- make a place-value chart to help you.

Solve each problem.

8. What is the value of the digit in the tens place in 1,076?

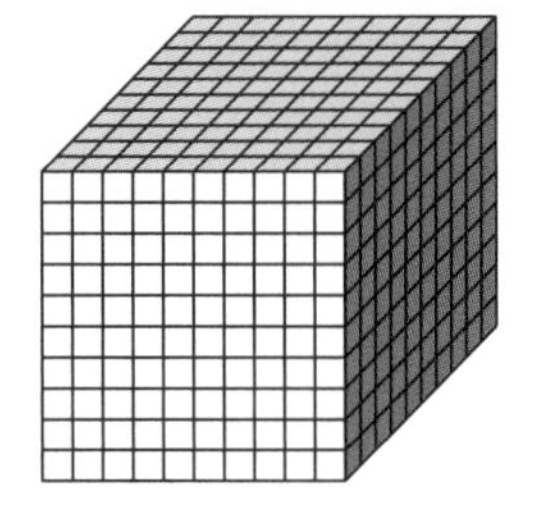
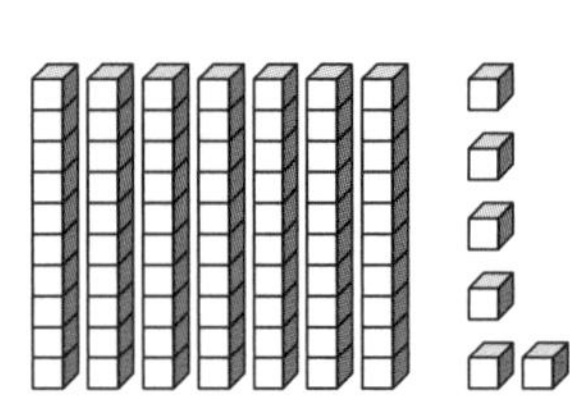

Ⓐ 7
Ⓑ 70
Ⓒ 700
Ⓓ 7000

9. What is another way to write 3,592?

Ⓐ 2 thousands + 5 hundreds + 19 tens + 2 ones
Ⓑ 2 thousands + 15 hundreds + 9 tens + 2 ones
Ⓒ 3 thousands + 5 hundreds + 19 tens + 2 ones
Ⓓ 3 thousands + 15 hundreds + 9 tens + 2 ones

10. Germaine has a roll of tape that is 14 hundred inches long. How long is the tape?

Ⓐ 14 inches
Ⓑ 140 inches
Ⓒ 1,400 inches
Ⓓ 14,000 inches

11. Which place-value chart shows 8 thousands + 4 hundreds + 7 tens + 9 ones?

Ⓐ

Thousands	Hundreds	Tens	Ones
4	8	7	9

Ⓑ

Thousands	Hundreds	Tens	Ones
8	4	9	7

Ⓒ

Thousands	Hundreds	Tens	Ones
8	4	7	9

Ⓓ

Thousands	Hundreds	Tens	Ones
7	4	8	9

12. A school building has 18 hundred students. How many students are there?

Ⓐ 18

Ⓑ 180

Ⓒ 800

Ⓓ 1,800

13. What is the value of the hundreds digit in 3,084?

Ⓐ 0

Ⓑ 80

Ⓒ 84

Ⓓ 3,000

14. The place-value chart shows 7,013. How can you write this number by regrouping 1 thousand?

Thousands	Hundreds	Tens	Ones
7	0	1	3

____ thousands + ____ hundreds + ____ ten + ____ ones

15. What is another way to write 3,681 if you regroup 1 thousand as 10 hundreds?

Thousands	Hundreds	Tens	Ones
3	6	8	1

Use pictures, words, or numbers to show your work.

Solution: _____ thousands + _____ hundreds + _____ tens + _____ one

Explain how you found your answer.

____

____

____

____

Lesson 2 ADD AND SUBTRACT

PART ONE: Learn About Using Place Value to Add

How can you use place value to add numbers?

Explore

Place value helps you **regroup** to find the **sum** of 2-digit numbers.

1. Add the ones. **2.** Regroup. **3.** Add the tens.	1 53 + 29 82 ← sum

How can place value help you find the sum of 3-digit numbers?

Think

Find 234 + 328.

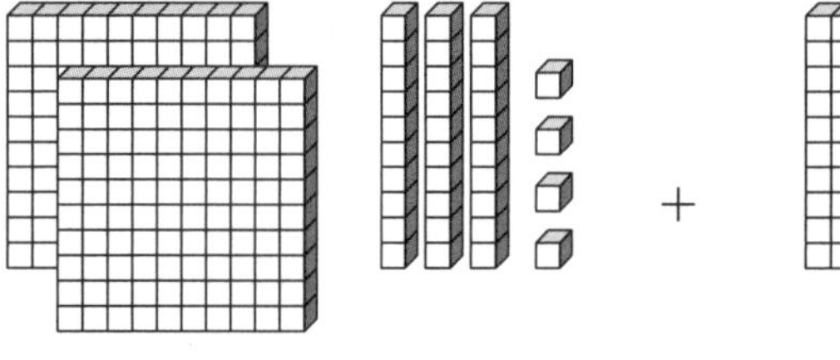

+

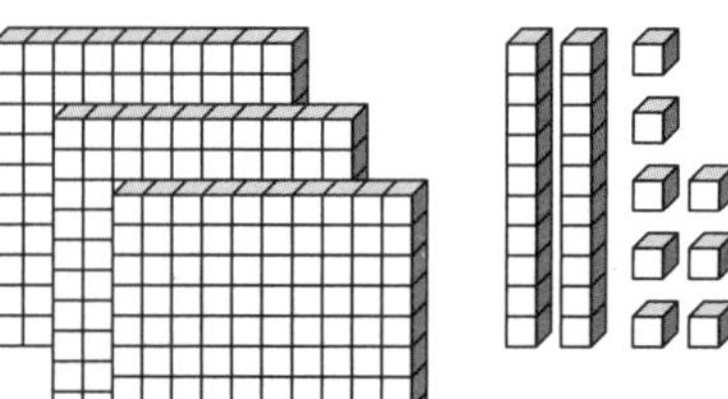

How many ones blocks are there in all? 12

How many tens blocks are there in all? 5

How many hundreds blocks are there in all? 5

Connect

Add the ones.	Add the tens.	Add the hundreds.
4 ones + 8 ones = 12 ones	3 tens + 2 tens = 5 tens	
Regroup. 12 ones = 1 ten 2 ones	Add regrouped ten. 5 tens + 1 ten = 6 tens	2 hundreds + 3 hundreds = 5 hundreds
1 ← 1 ten 234 + 328 2 ← 2 ones	1 234 + 328 62 ← 6 tens	1 234 + 328 562 ← 5 hundreds

Let's Talk

Suppose you added 394 to 234. How would the way you add the numbers change?

Fill in the blanks. Solve the problem.

What is 146 + 378?

- Set up the problem.

146
+ 378

- Add the ones.

☐
1 4 6
+ 3 7 8

____ ones + ____ ones = ____ ones

Regroup 10 ones as 1 ten.

☐ ← ____ ones = 1 ten + ____ ones

- Add the tens.

☐ 1
1 4 6
+ 3 7 8

1 ten + ____ ten(s) + ____ ten(s) = ____ tens

Regroup 10 tens as 1 hundred.

☐4 ← ____ tens = 1 hundred + ____ tens

- Add the hundreds.

1 1
1 4 6
+ 3 7 8

☐2 4 ← 1 hundred + ____ hundred(s) + ____ hundred(s)

= ____ hundreds

Solution: 146 + 378 = ______

Regroup 14 ones as 1 ten and 4 ones.
Regroup 12 tens as 1 hundred and 2 tens.

Now, use what you know to solve this problem.

1.

255
+ 182

Ⓐ 337
Ⓑ 347
Ⓒ 437
Ⓓ 447

PART TWO: Learn About Using Place Value to Subtract

How can you use place value to subtract numbers?

Explore

You use place value to find the **difference** of 2-digit numbers.

1. Subtract the ones. **2.** Regroup tens as ones. **3.** Subtract the tens.	3 15 ~~4~~~~5~~ − 28 17 ← difference

How can place value help you regroup to subtract 3-digit numbers?

Think

Find 636 − 454.

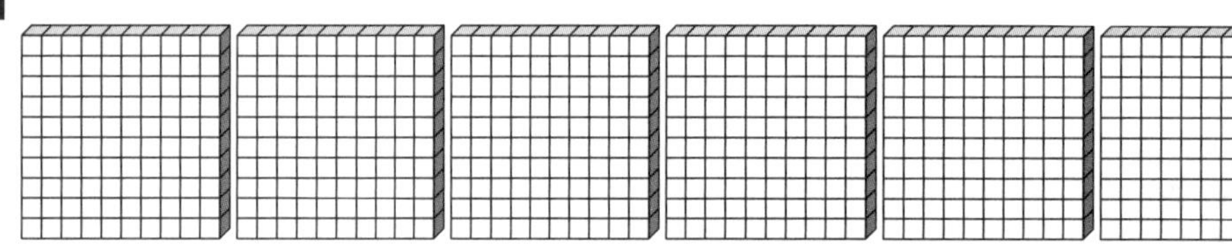

Are there enough ones in 636 to subtract the 4 ones in 454? yes

Are there enough tens in 636 to subtract the 5 tens in 454? no

Regroup 1 hundred as 10 tens. After you regroup, there are 5 hundreds 13 tens.

Connect

Subtract the ones.	Subtract the tens.	Subtract the hundreds.
6 ones − 4 ones = 2 ones	3 < 5 Regroup 1 hundred. 10 tens + 3 tens = 13 tens 13 tens − 5 tens = 8 tens	5 hundreds − 4 hundreds = 1 hundred
636 − 454 2	5 13 ~~6~~~~3~~6 − 454 82	5 13 ~~6~~~~3~~6 − 454 182

Let's Talk

If you changed the problem to 636 − 478, would you follow the same steps to subtract? Why or why not?

Fill in the blanks. Solve the problem.

There are 304 cans of vegetables on a grocery shelf.
Customers buy 178 cans. How many cans are left?

- Set up the problem.

```
  304
- 178
-----
```

- Subtract the ones.

  4 ones $<$ 8 ones. Regroup 1 ten as 10 ones.
  There are 0 tens, so regroup 1 hundred as 10 tens.
  Then regroup 1 ten as 10 ones.

- Subtract the tens.

```
    9
  2 10 14
  3  0  4
− 1  7  8
---------
   [ ]  6
```

____ tens − ____ tens = ____ tens

- Subtract the hundreds.

```
    9
  2 10 14
  3  0  4
− 1  7  8
---------
 [ ] 2  6
```

____ hundreds − ____ hundred = ____ hundred

Solution: 304 − 178 = _______

You may need to regroup tens as ones, but there are 0 tens. So, first regroup 1 hundred as 10 tens. Then regroup 1 ten as 10 ones.

Now, use what you know to solve this problem.

2.

```
  502
- 135
-----
```

Solve the problem. Then read why each answer choice is correct or not correct.

Solve

One day 444 people visited the state park. By late afternoon, 218 people had left. How many people were still at the park?

$$\begin{array}{r} 444 \\ -\ 218 \\ \hline \end{array}$$

Ⓐ 126

Ⓑ 226

Ⓒ 236

Ⓓ 244

Check

Check to see if you chose the correct answer.

4 ones < 8 ones

To subtract the ones, you need to regroup 1 ten as 10 ones. Then subtract the ones, the tens, and the hundreds.

$$\begin{array}{r} {\scriptstyle 3\ 14} \\ 4\not{4}\not{4} \\ -\ 218 \\ \hline 226 \end{array}$$

So, the correct answer is Ⓑ.

Why are the other answer choices not correct?

Ⓐ 126	The hundreds do not need to be regrouped.
Ⓒ 236	The number of tens should be 1 less because 1 ten is regrouped as 10 ones.
Ⓓ 234	The 8 ones need to be subtracted from the 4 ones, not the 4 ones from the 8 ones.

Your Turn **Solve each problem. Use the hints to avoid mistakes.**

- When adding, regroup when the sum of the digits in any place is greater than 9.
- When subtracting, regroup when the bottom digit is greater than the top digit in any place.
- When there are 0 tens to regroup as ones, first regroup hundreds and then regroup tens.

3.

$$\begin{array}{r} 495 \\ +\ 126 \\ \hline \end{array}$$

Ⓐ 511

Ⓑ 521

Ⓒ 621

Ⓓ 711

4. There were 217 people at a play. Then 136 more people came. How many people were at the play in all?

$$\begin{array}{r} 217 \\ +\ 136 \\ \hline \end{array}$$

Ⓐ 343

Ⓑ 353

Ⓒ 443

Ⓓ 453

5.

$$\begin{array}{r} 426 \\ -\ 237 \\ \hline \end{array}$$

Ⓐ 189

Ⓑ 211

Ⓒ 289

Ⓓ 299

6. In the morning, there were 970 books on the shelves at the library. During the day, people took out 533 books. How many books were left on the shelves?

$$\begin{array}{r} 970 \\ -\ 533 \\ \hline \end{array}$$

Ⓐ 337

Ⓑ 347

Ⓒ 433

Ⓓ 437

Study the model. It is a good example of a written answer.

Student Model

Show

It took Miriam 609 minutes to travel to her grandmother's house. Then it took another 359 minutes to travel to her aunt's house. How many minutes did Miriam travel in all?

Use pictures, words, or numbers to show your work.

$$\begin{array}{r} {}^{1} \\ 609 \\ +\ 359 \\ \hline 968 \end{array}$$

9 ones + 9 ones = 18 ones

Regroup 18 ones as 1 ten 8 ones.

☑ The student shows each step.

Solution: 968 minutes

☑ The student correctly answers the question asked.

Explain

Explain how you got your answer.

I added the ones first. 9 + 9 = 18, so I regrouped 18 as 1 ten 8 ones. I added the tens next. 1 ten + 0 tens + 5 tens = 6 tens. This sum is less than 10 tens, so I did not need to regroup hundreds. I added the hundreds. 6 hundreds + 3 hundreds = 9 hundreds

☑ The student gives important details about how to find the total.

☑ The student uses the math words *ones, tens, sum, hundreds, add,* and *regroup.*

Your Turn **Solve the problem. Use what you learned from the model.**

7. Keisha has 609 shells in her shell collection. Billy has 359 shells. How many more shells does Keisha have than Billy?

   Use pictures, words, or numbers to show your work.

CHECKLIST

Did you . . .

- ☐ show each step?
- ☐ answer the question asked?
- ☐ give important details?
- ☐ use math words?

Solution: ______ shells

Explain how you got your answer.

____

____

____

____

____

As you solve addition and subtractions problems, remember to
- regroup when adding more than 9 tens or 9 ones.
- regroup when there are not enough ones or tens in the top digit to subtract from the bottom digit.

Solve each problem.

8.

$$\begin{array}{r} 371 \\ -\ 105 \\ \hline \end{array}$$

Ⓐ 176

Ⓑ 265

Ⓒ 266

Ⓓ 274

9. Kim is rolling pennies to take to the bank. She has two piggy banks. One bank has 189 pennies. The other bank has 305 pennies. How many pennies does Kim have in all?

Ⓐ 484 pennies

Ⓑ 494 pennies

Ⓒ 584 pennies

Ⓓ 594 pennies

10. There are 585 students at Rhonda's school and 319 students at Sam's school. How many more students are there at Rhonda's school?

Ⓐ 166 students

Ⓑ 176 students

Ⓒ 261 students

Ⓓ 266 students

11.

$$\begin{array}{r} 476 \\ +\ 458 \\ \hline \end{array}$$

Ⓐ 824

Ⓑ 834

Ⓒ 924

Ⓓ 934

12. $403 - 259 = \blacksquare$

Ⓐ 144

Ⓑ 154

Ⓒ 254

Ⓓ 256

13. $747 + 166 = \blacksquare$

Ⓐ 803

Ⓑ 813

Ⓒ 903

Ⓓ 913

14. A farmer planted 187 tomato seeds. Then he planted 644 soybean seeds. How many seeds did the farmer plant in all?

_______ seeds

15. One baby elephant weighs 711 pounds. Another baby elephant weighs 234 pounds. How much heavier is the first elephant than the second elephant?

Use pictures, words, or numbers to show your work.

Solution: _______ pounds

Explain how you got your answer.

____

____

____

____

____

Lesson 3 MULTIPLICATION CONCEPTS

PART ONE: Learn About Equal Groups

How can you find the total of equal groups?

Addition is used to find the total number of items in several groups.

   $1 + 2 + 3 = 6$

What if all the groups have the same number of items?

Think

Multiplication is a quick way to find the total of **equal groups**.

How many groups of hearts are shown? ___3___

How many hearts are in each group? ___2___

You have ___3___ equal groups. Each has ___2___ hearts.

Connect

Repeated addition helps you understand multiplication.

   3 groups of 2

Add 2 three times. $2 + 2 + 2 = 6$	OR	**Multiply** 3 times 2. $3 \times 2 = 6$

Let's Talk

Can you use multiplication to find the total number of diamonds?

Why or why not?

Fill in the blanks. Solve the problem.

Selena has 4 cans of tennis balls. Each can has 3 tennis balls.

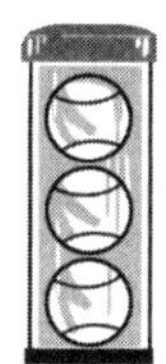 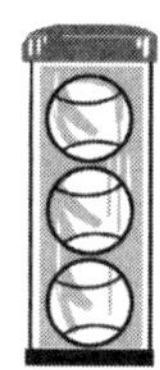 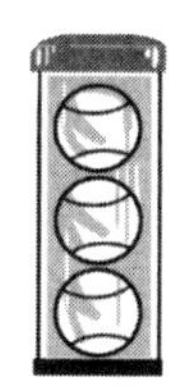 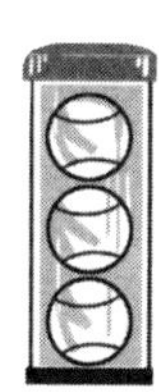

What is the total number of tennis balls?

- How many cans are there? _______

  How many tennis balls are in each can? _______

- You can use repeated addition to find the total.

  There are _______ items in each of the 4 groups.

  Add 3 four times. ____ + ____ + ____ + ____ = ____

- You can also use multiplication to find the total.

  There are 4 groups of _______ .

  Multiply 4 times 3. ____ × ____ = ____

Solution: There are _______ tennis balls in all.

Now, use what you know to solve this problem.

1. Which two number sentences can you use to find the total?

Ⓐ 6 + 6 + 6 = ▢ and 6 × 6 = ▢

Ⓑ 6 + 6 + 6 = ▢ and 3 × 6 = ▢

Ⓒ 3 + 6 = ▢ and 3 × 6 = ▢

Ⓓ 3 + 3 + 3 = ▢ and 3 × 3 = ▢

How can you use an array to help you multiply?

Explore

You can use multiplication to find the total of equal groups.
The rows of an **array** show equal groups.
Each **row** has the same number of items.

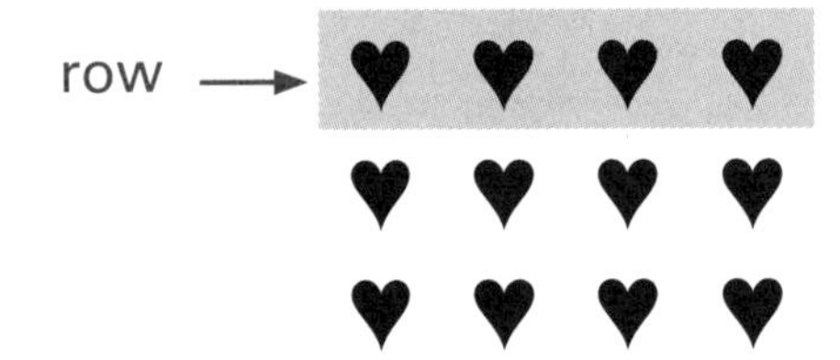

Think

How many rows are in the array above? 3

How many items are in each row? 4

The array has 3 rows of 4 hearts.

Connect

Multiply 3 × 4 to find the total number of hearts.

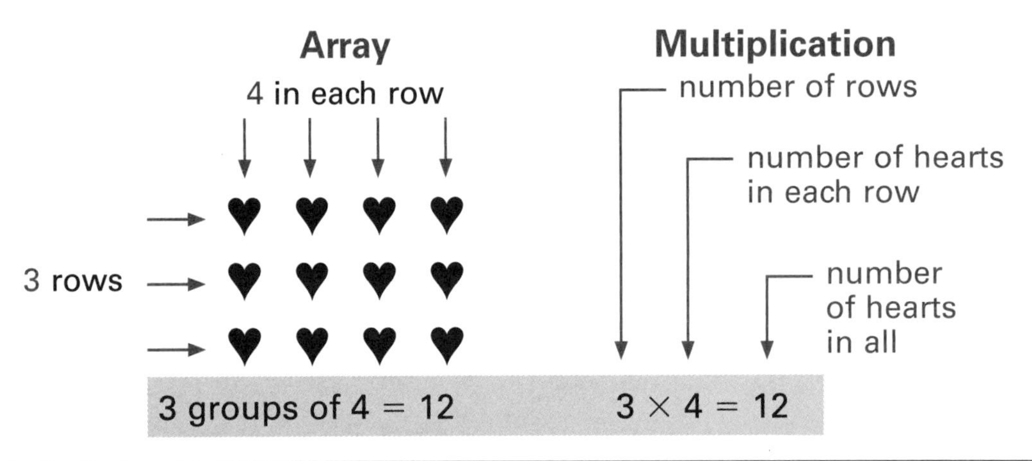

Let's Talk

Tell how this array is like the array above and how it is different.

What do you notice about the total number of hearts in each array?

Fill in the blanks. Solve the problem.

Manny bought a sheet of stamps. The sheet has 5 rows of stamps. Each row has 4 stamps. How many stamps did Manny buy in all?

- You have to find the total of 5 groups of 4 stamps.

  You can draw an array to show the equal groups.

  How many rows should the array have? _______

  How many items should be in each row? _______

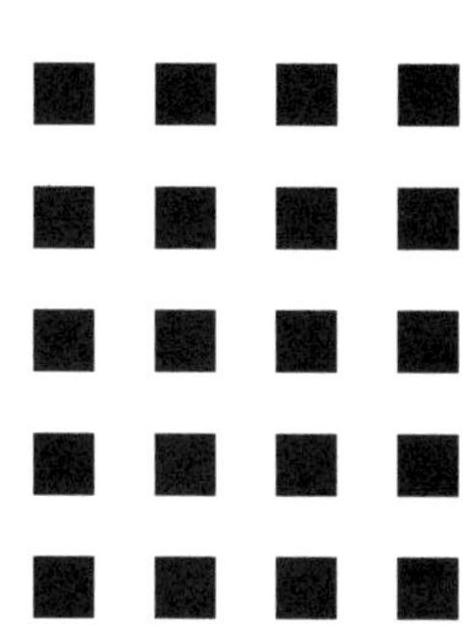

- 5 rows of 4 is the same as _____ $\times$ _____.

  Multiply to find the total number of stamps.

  _____ $\times$ _____ $=$ _____

Solution: Manny bought _______ stamps in all.

Your Turn **Now, use what you know to solve this problem.**

2. Draw an array to find the product of 2×6. Use the grid to help you line up items in the rows.

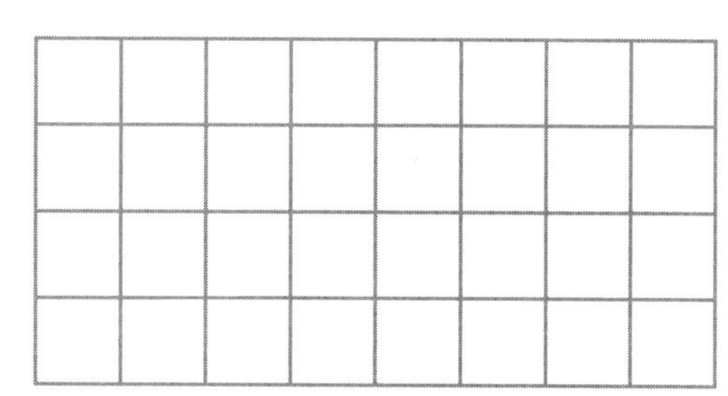

$2 \times 6 =$ _______

Solve the problem. Then read why each answer choice is correct or not correct.

Solve

A gym teacher stores basketballs in 3 bags. Each bag holds 7 basketballs.

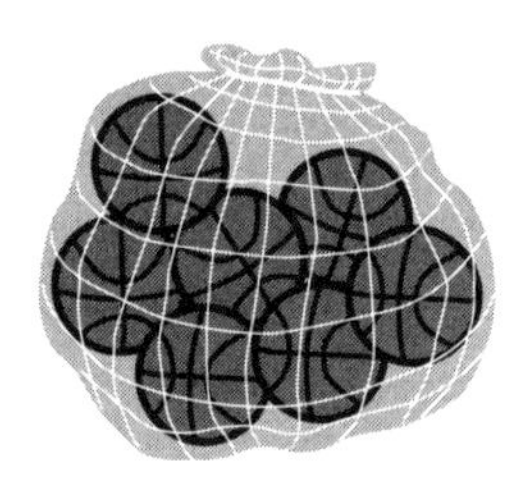
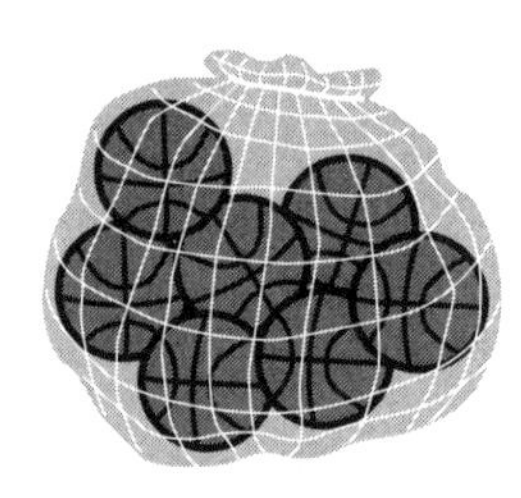
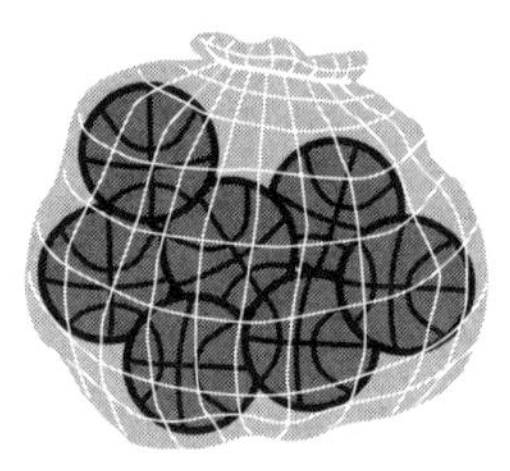

Which number sentence shows the total number of basketballs?

Ⓐ $3 + 3 + 3 = 9$

Ⓑ $3 \times 8 = 24$

Ⓒ $3 + 7 = 10$

Ⓓ $3 \times 7 = 21$

Check

Check to see if you chose the correct answer.

There are 3 groups of 7 basketballs.
3 groups of 7 is the same as 3×7.
$3 \times 7 = 21$

So, the correct answer is Ⓓ.

Why are the other answer choices not correct?

Ⓐ $3 + 3 + 3 = 9$	The number of basketballs in each group should be added, not the number of groups.
Ⓑ $3 \times 8 = 24$	There are 7 basketballs, not 8.
Ⓒ $3 + 7 = 10$	The two factors should be multiplied, not added.

Your Turn **Solve each problem. Use the hints to avoid mistakes.**

- Identify the number of groups and the number of items in each one.
- Count the groups and items carefully.
- Use $\times$ to multiply numbers.

3. Shaun works in a party store. He is blowing up 2 bunches of balloons. Each bunch has 6 balloons.

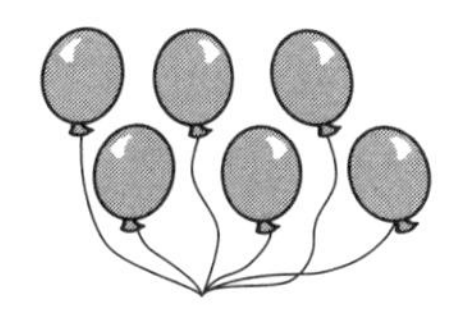 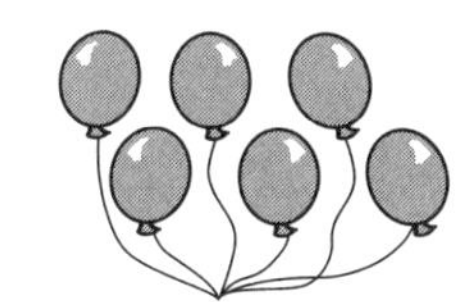

Which number sentence can be used to find the total number of balloons?

Ⓐ $6 + 6 + 6 = \square$

Ⓑ $6 \times 6 = \square$

Ⓒ $2 \times 6 = \square$

Ⓓ $2 + 6 = \square$

4. A triangle is a shape with 3 sides.

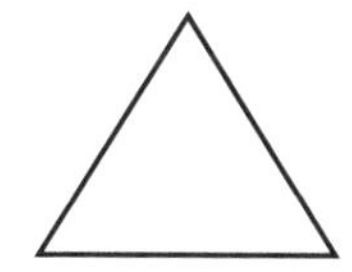

How many sides do 5 triangles have?

Ⓐ 15

Ⓑ 12

Ⓒ 10

Ⓓ 8

5. Sofia keeps beads in the plastic case shown below.

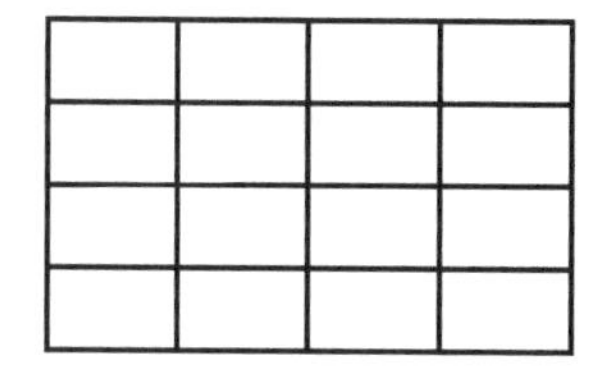

Which multiplication sentence is shown by this array?

Ⓐ $6 \times 6 = 36$

Ⓑ $4 \times 3 = 12$

Ⓒ $4 \times 4 = 16$

Ⓓ $5 \times 4 = 20$

6. Which two number sentences have the same answer?

Ⓐ $4 \times 9 = \square$
$9 + 9 + 9 + 9 = \square$

Ⓑ $4 \times 9 = \square$
$4 + 9 = \square$

Ⓒ $4 \times 9 = \square$
$4 + 4 + 4 + 4 = \square$

Ⓓ $9 \times 9 = \square$
$9 + 9 = \square$

Study the model. It is a good example of a written answer.

Student Model

Show

Sydney's uncle gave her 6 packs of baseball cards. Each pack has 5 cards in it. How many baseball cards does Sydney have in all?

Use pictures, words, or numbers to show your work.

6 groups of 5

$6 \times 5 = ?$

$5+5+5+5+5+5 = 30$

☑ The student shows each step.

Solution: 30 baseball cards

☑ The student correctly answers the question.

Explain

Explain how you got your answer.

There are 6 equal groups of cards. Each group has 5 cards. 6 groups of 5 is 6×5. I drew an array to help me find the product of 6×5. I drew 6 rows for the 6 groups and 5 rectangles in each row for the 5 cards. I saw there are 30 cards in all. I checked my answer by adding 5 six times.

☑ The student gives important details about the total.

☑ The student uses the math words *equal groups, array, product,* and *row.*

Your Turn **Solve the problem. Use what you learned from the model.**

7. The town's school buses are parked in a lot when they are not being used. The buses are parked in 3 rows. Each row has 8 buses. How many buses are parked in the lot each day?

Use pictures, words, or numbers to show your work.

CHECKLIST

Did you . . .

- ☐ show each step?
- ☐ answer the question asked?
- ☐ give important details?
- ☐ use math words?

Solution: ______ buses

Explain how you got your answer.

____

____

____

____

____

____

As you solve multiplication problems, you may want to
- draw pictures or an array to show equal groups.
- use repeated addition to check your work.

Solve each problem.

8. Which number sentence can be used to find the total number of pens?

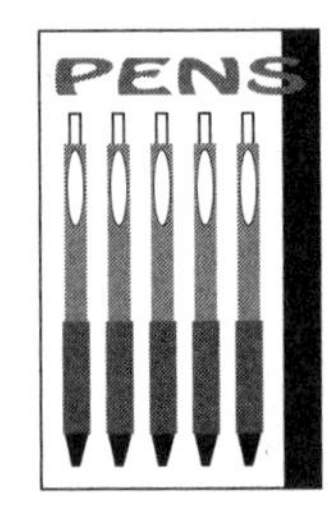

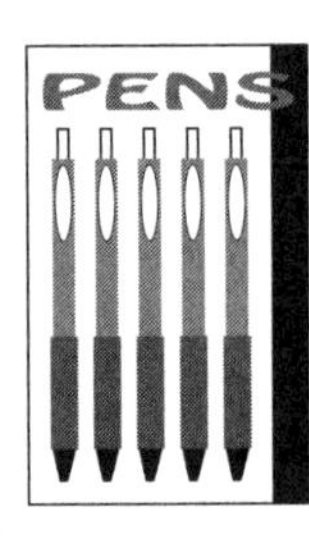

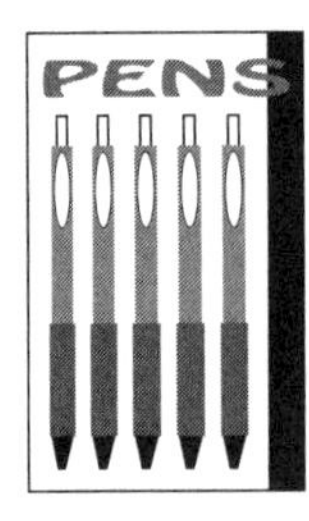

Ⓐ $5 + 5 = \square$

Ⓑ $3 + 3 + 3 + 3 = \square$

Ⓒ $3 \times 5 = \square$

Ⓓ $3 + 5 = \square$

9. Which array shows 6×4?

Ⓐ 

Ⓒ 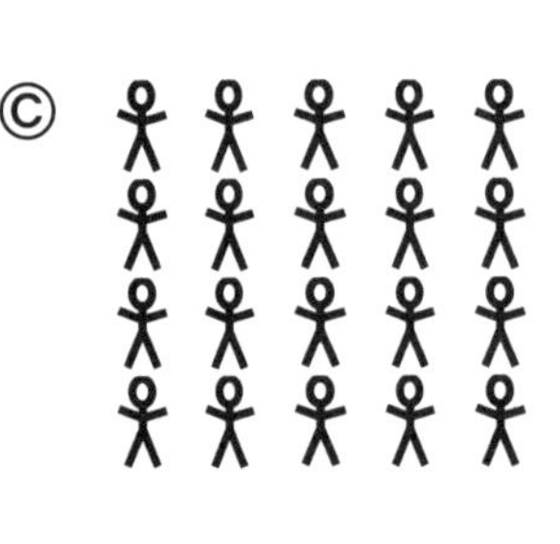

Ⓑ 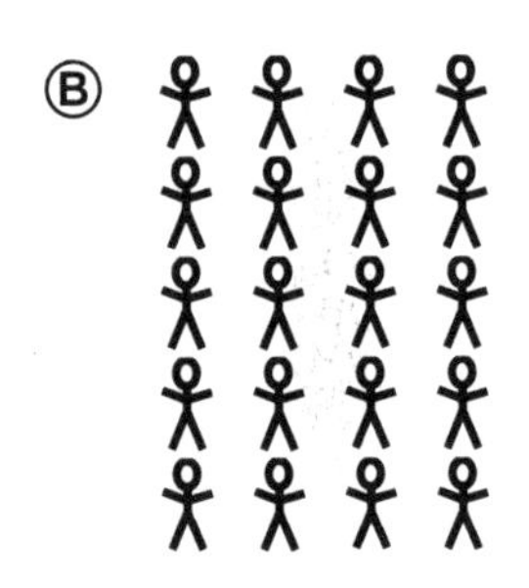

Ⓓ 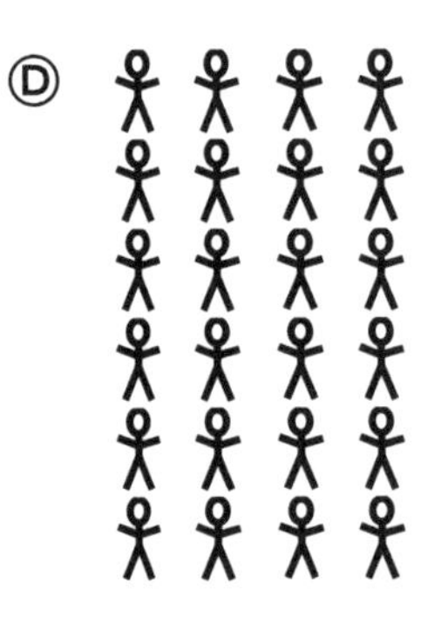

10. Nia helped set up for a meeting after school. She set up 4 rows of chairs. There were 7 chairs in each row.

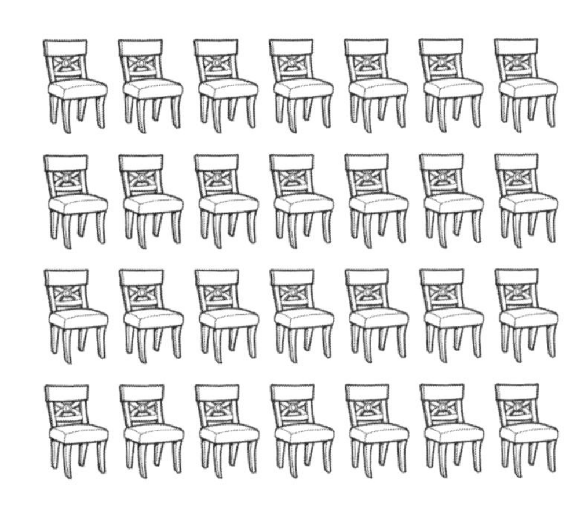

Which multiplication sentence is shown by the array of chairs?

Ⓐ $7 \times 3 = 21$

Ⓑ $4 \times 7 = 28$

Ⓒ $5 \times 7 = 35$

Ⓓ $4 \times 8 = 32$

11. Peter filled 9 pages of a photo album. Each page of the album holds 2 photos. How many photos in all did Peter put in the album?

Ⓐ 18

Ⓑ 16

Ⓒ 11

Ⓓ 9

12. A grocer set up a display of melons. The display has 5 rows. Each row has 5 melons. What is the total number of melons?

Ⓐ 10

Ⓑ 20

Ⓒ 25

Ⓓ 30

13. Laura served 4 bowls of berries for dessert. She put 8 berries in each bowl. How many berries did Laura serve in all?

Ⓐ 12

Ⓑ 16

Ⓒ 24

Ⓓ 32

14. Jamal is a woodworker. He is carving legs for 6 new stools. Each stool will have 3 legs. How many legs will Jamal carve in all?

Write an addition sentence and a multiplication sentence to show the total.

Addition sentence:

____

Multiplication sentence:

____

15. Caleb baked 4 tins of muffins. Each tin has 6 muffins. How many muffins did Caleb bake in all?

Use pictures, words, or numbers to show your work.

Solution: ______ muffins

Explain how you found your answer.

____

____

____

____

Lesson 4 FACT STRATEGIES

PART ONE: Learn About Skip Counting and Multiplication

How can skip counting help you learn basic facts?

Explore

When you **skip count**, you count up by a number other than 1.

To skip count by 2, you add 2 each time: 0, 2, 4, 6, 8, 10, . . .

To skip count by 5, you add 5 each time: 0, 5, 10, 15, 20, 25, . . .

How can skip counting help you learn **multiplication facts**?

Think

You can use a **number line** to skip count.

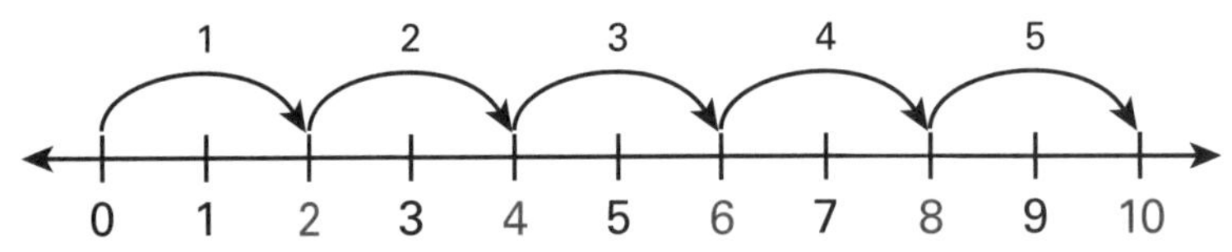

When you jump by 2 three times you land on 6. $3 \times 2 =$ 6

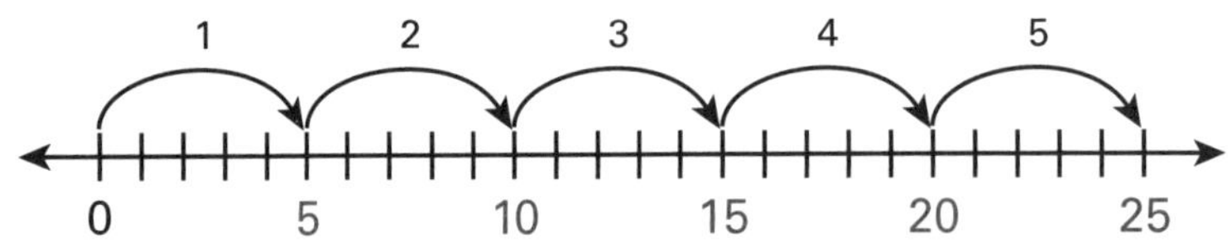

When you jump by 5 three times you land on 15. $3 \times 5 =$ 15

Connect

Skip counting by 2 helps you find the **product** of any number times 2.

Multiply × 2	1×2=	2×2=	3×2=	4×2=	5×2=
Skip count by 2	2	4	6	8	10

Skip counting by 5 helps you find the product of any number times 5.

Multiply × 5	1×5=	2×5=	3×5=	4×5=	5×5=
Skip count by 5	5	10	15	20	25

Let's Talk

Use the first number line in Think to find 5×2. Then use the second number line to find the multiplication fact that has the same product. What do you notice?

Fill in the blanks. Solve the problem.

Find 6×3. Use the number line to help you.

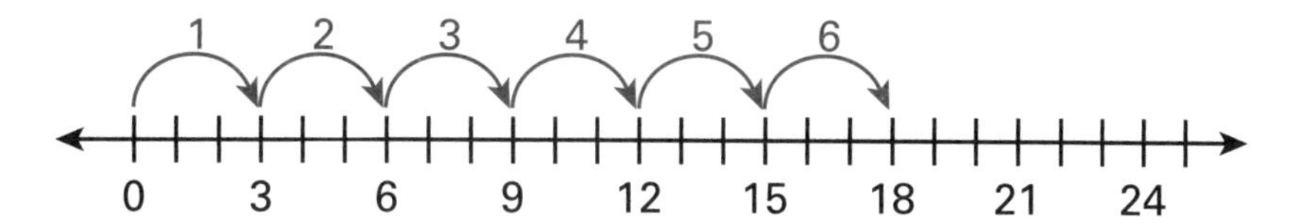

- Skip count by 3. Start at zero. Make _______ jumps of 3.
- Number the jumps on the number line.
  Write out the numbers you land on with each jump.

  0, _______, _______, _______, _______, _______, _______
- What is the last number you wrote? _______

Solution: $6 \times 3 =$ _______

Draw "jumps" on the number line to help you skip count.
The numbers you multiply are the **factors**.

$3 \times 2 = 6$

The total is the product.

Your Turn **Now, use what you know to solve this problem.**

1. Find 7×3. Use the number line above to help you.

Ⓐ 4

Ⓑ 10

Ⓒ 21

Ⓓ 24

PART TWO: Learn About Doubling and Multiplication

How can doubling help you learn multiplication facts?

Explore

There are different ways to learn multiplication facts.

$3 \times 2 = 6$		
Repeated Addition	Arrays	Skip Counting
$2 + 2 + 2 = 6$	●● ●● ●● 3 groups of 2 = 6	Count by 2 three times. 2, 4, 6

How can you use facts you know to learn other facts?

Think

Find 2×7.

2×7 { ●●●●●●● ← 7; ●●●●●●● ← 7 }

2×7 is double 7. 7 + 7 = 14

Connect

Multiplying any number by 2 is the same as **doubling** the number. You can use doubling of facts you know to learn new facts.

4×7 { ●●●●●●● / ●●●●●●● ← 2×7; ●●●●●●● / ●●●●●●● ← 2×7 }

$4 \times 7 = (2 \times 7) + (2 \times 7)$
$4 \times 7 = 14 + 14$
$4 \times 7 = 28$

4 is double 2, so 4×7 is double 2×7.

Let's Talk

You know that $2 \times 9 = 18$. Use doubling to find a new multiplication fact.

Fill in the blanks. Solve the problem.

Mateo knows that $4 \times 7 = 28$. How can he use this fact and doubling to find 8×7?

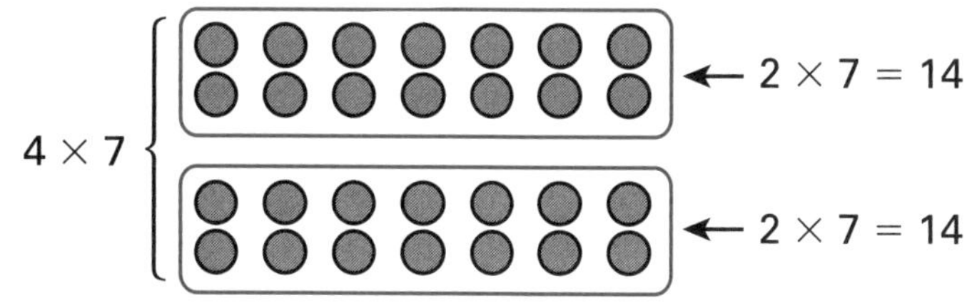

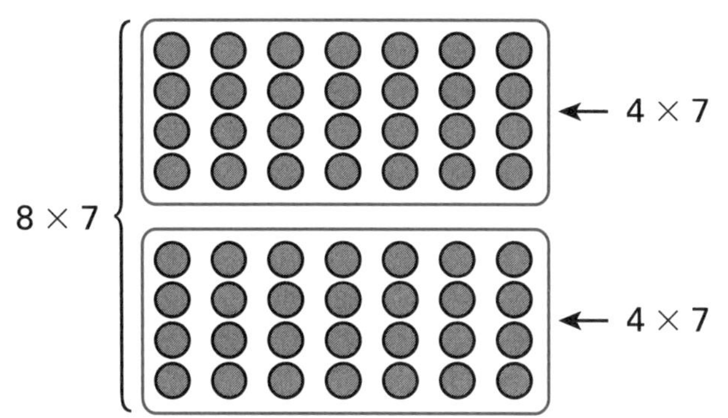

- 8 is double _______, so 8×7 is double _______ $\times$ 7.

  $8 \times 7 = (\_\_\_\_ \times 7) + (\_\_\_\_ \times 7)$

- Find the products.

  $4 \times 7 =$ _______

  $8 \times 7 =$ ____ + ____

- Add.

  $28 + 28 =$ _______

Solution: $8 \times 7 =$ _______

Your Turn **Now, use what you know to solve this problem.**

2. How can you use the fact $4 \times 3 = 12$ to find 8×3?

$8 \times 3 = (\_\_\_\_ \times \_\_\_\_) + (\_\_\_\_ \times \_\_\_\_)$

$8 \times 3 =$ ____ + ____

$8 \times 3 =$ _______

Solve the problem. Then read why each answer choice is correct or not correct.

Solve

At Jeremy's fruit stand, there are 6 bags of apples. Each bag has 5 apples. How many apples are there in all?

Ⓐ 11

Ⓑ 25

Ⓒ 30

Ⓓ 35

Check

Check to see if you chose the correct answer.

To find 6×5, skip count by 5 six times. A number line can help.

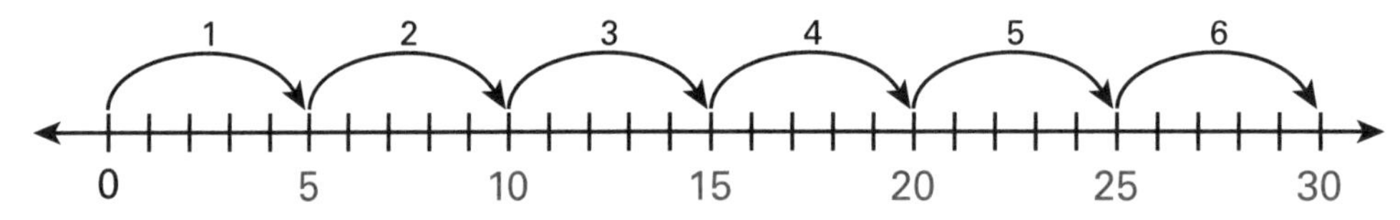

Jumping by 5 six times lands on 30.

$6 \times 5 = 30$

So, the correct answer is Ⓒ.

Why are the other answer choices not correct?

Ⓐ 11	The two factors should be multiplied, not added.
Ⓑ 25	This is the result of skip counting by 5 five times, not six times.
Ⓓ 35	This is the result of skip counting by 5 seven times, not six times.

Your Turn **Solve each problem. Use the hints to avoid mistakes.**

- If you use a number line, be sure to skip count the correct number of times to find a multiplication fact.
- If you use doubling, be sure to add the products together to get the final product.

Use the number line to help you solve problems 3–6.

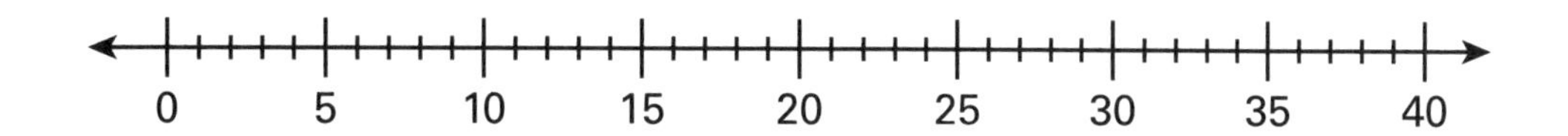

3. There are 9 students. Each student has 2 pencils. How many pencils are there in all?

$9 \times 2 = \blacksquare$

Ⓐ 7

Ⓑ 9

Ⓒ 11

Ⓓ 18

4. Nadia has 4 flowers. Each flower has 4 petals. How many petals are there?

$4 \times 4 = \blacksquare$

Ⓐ 8

Ⓑ 12

Ⓒ 16

Ⓓ 20

5. There are 7 rows. Each row has 5 chairs. How many chairs are there in all?

$7 \times 5 = \blacksquare$

Ⓐ 20

Ⓑ 25

Ⓒ 30

Ⓓ 35

6. A bookcase has 4 shelves. There are 7 books on each shelf. How many books are there altogether?

$4 \times 7 = \blacksquare$

Ⓐ 28

Ⓑ 24

Ⓒ 16

Ⓓ 11

Study the model. It is a good example of a written answer.

Student Model

Show

Ling has 4 bags and puts 9 marbles in each bag. How many marbles in all did she put in the bags?

Use pictures, words, or numbers to show your work.

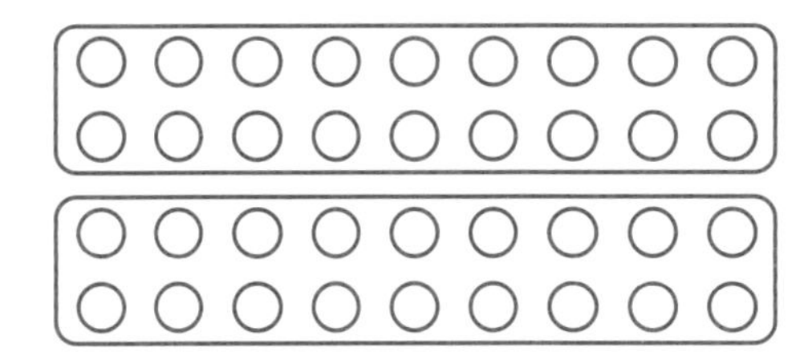

$4 \times 9 = (2 \times 9) + (2 \times 9)$

$4 \times 9 = 18 + 18$

$4 \times 9 = 36$

☑ The student shows each step.

Explain

Solution: Ling put 36 marbles into the bags.

☑ The student correctly answers the question asked.

Explain how you got your answer.

There are 4 bags and each has 9 marbles, so I drew an array to show 4 equal groups of 9. I can multiply 4×9 to find the total. I doubled a known fact to solve the problem. I know that $2 \times 9 = 18$, and 4×9 is double that. $18 + 18 = 36$. So, Ling put 36 marbles in all in the bags.

☑ The student gives important details about how to find the product.

☑ The student uses math words like *equal groups, multiply, total,* and *double.*

Your Turn **Solve the problem. Use what you learned from the model.**

7. Pedro is making a comic book. The book has 9 pages. He draws 3 pictures on each page. How many pictures did he draw in all?

Use pictures, words, or numbers to show your work.

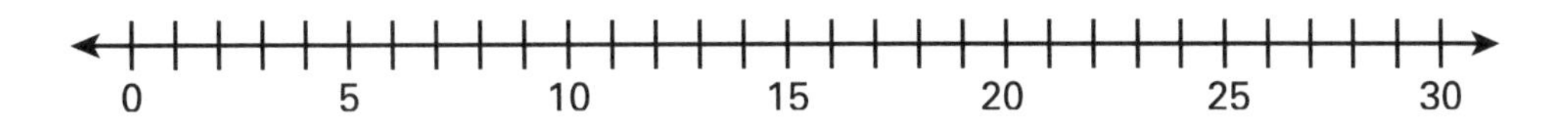

Solution: Pedro drew _______ pictures.

Explain how you got your answer.

____

____

____

____

____

____

As you solve problems with multiplication facts, you may want to
- skip count using a number line.
- double facts you already know.

Solve each problem.

8. There are 7 rows of tomato plants in a garden. Each row has 5 tomato plants. How many tomato plants are there in all?

$7 \times 5 = \square$

Ⓐ 35

Ⓑ 30

Ⓒ 28

Ⓓ 12

9. Which fact can you double to find the product below?

$8 \times 7 = \square$

Ⓐ 2×7

Ⓑ 8×6

Ⓒ 4×7

Ⓓ 4×8

10. Which problem is shown on the number line?

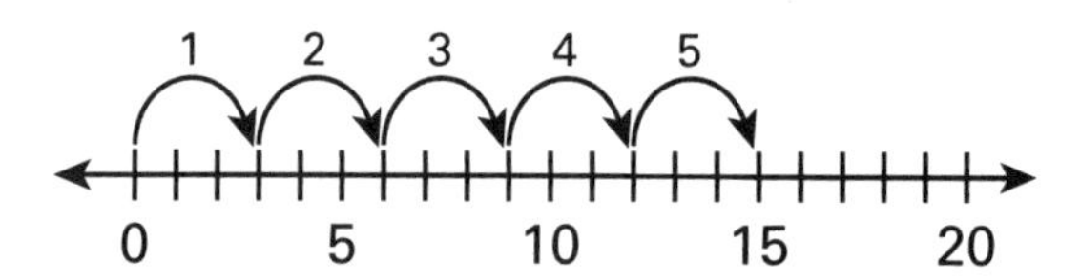

Ⓐ $5 + 3$

Ⓑ 6×3

Ⓒ 5×3

Ⓓ 5×4

11. Which fact can you double to find the product below?

$4 \times 6 = \square$

Ⓐ 4×5

Ⓑ 2×6

Ⓒ 4×12

Ⓓ 2×3

12. $4 \times 5 = $ ▒

Ⓐ 10
Ⓑ 12
Ⓒ 15
Ⓓ 20

13. $8 \times 6 = $ ▒

Ⓐ 48
Ⓑ 40
Ⓒ 24
Ⓓ 14

14. Skip count to find 7×2.

2, ____, ____, ____, ____,

____, ____

$7 \times 2 = $ ____

15. Kylie put her stuffed animals in rows. She made 8 rows with 4 animals in each row. How many stuffed animals does Kylie have in all?

Use pictures, words, or numbers to show your work.

Solution: Kylie has ______ stuffed animals.

Explain how you got your answer.

Lesson 5 MORE FACT STRATEGIES

PART ONE: Learn About Multiplication Facts for 3 and 6

How can you use known facts to learn 3s and 6s facts?

Explore

Doubling facts you know can help you learn new facts.

Use a 2s fact to find 4×8.

$4 \times 8 = (2 \times 8) + (2 \times 8)$
$4 \times 8 = 16 + 16$
$4 \times 8 = 32$

4 is double 2,
so 4×8 is double 2×8.

What is another way to use facts you know to find other facts?

Think

The **array** shows __3__ rows of __8__,
or __3__ $\times$ __8__.

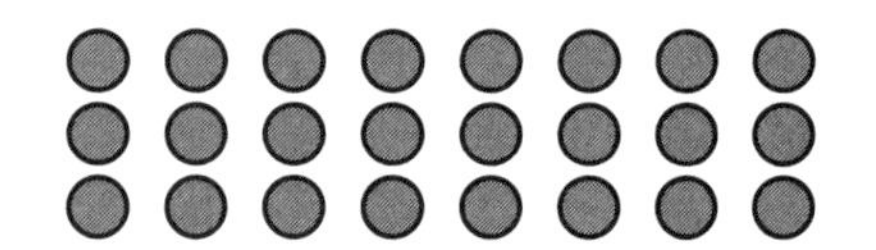

Connect

Use facts you know to find 3×8.

Think of 3 as $2 + 1$.

$3 \times 8 = (2 \times 8) + (1 \times 8)$

$3 \times 8 = 16 + 8$

$3 \times 8 = 24$

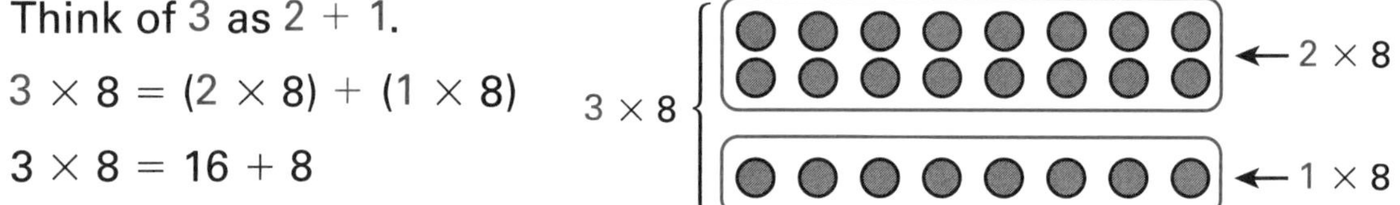

Because $3 = 2 + 1$, you can use 2s facts and 1s facts to find the 3s fact.

Let's Talk

You can think of 3×10 as 2 groups of 10 plus 1 more group of 10.
How can you use a 2s fact and a 1s fact to write 3×10?

Fill in the blanks. Solve the problem.

What is 6×4?

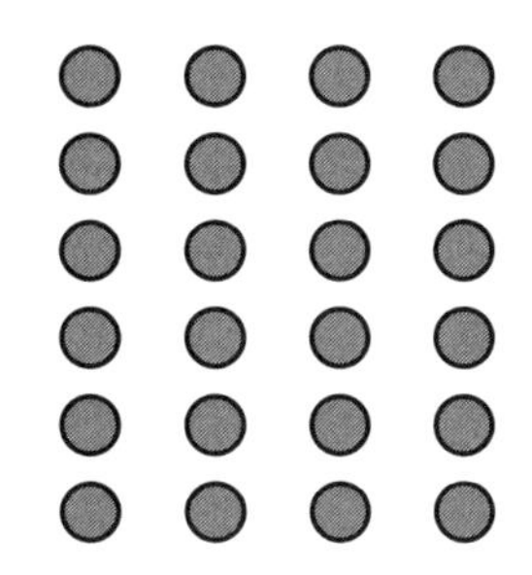

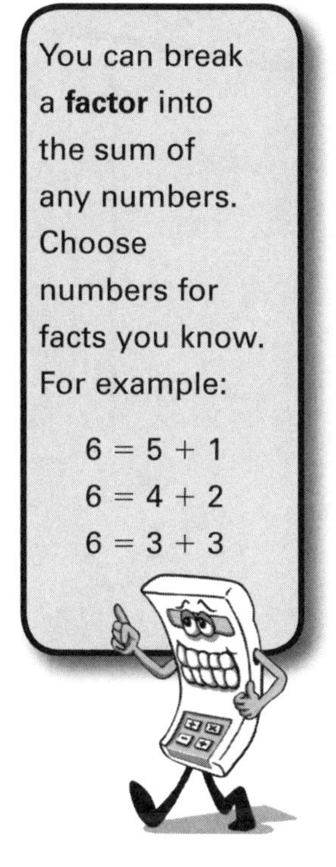

- Think of 6 as $5 + 1$.
- Circle rows on the array to show ____ rows of ____ and ____ row of ____.
- $6 \times 4 = (\_\_\_\_ \times 4) + (\_\_\_\_ \times 4)$

  $6 \times 4 = \_\_\_\_ + \_\_\_\_$

  $6 \times 4 = \_\_\_\_$

Solution: $6 \times 4 = \_\_\_\_$

Your Turn **Now, use what you know to solve this problem.**

1. What is 3×7? Use the array to help you.

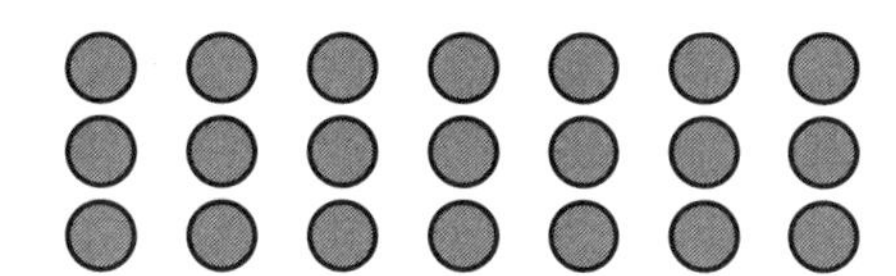

Ⓐ 7
Ⓑ 10
Ⓒ 14
Ⓓ 21

How can you use known facts to learn 7s and 9s facts?

Explore

You can use facts you know to find facts for 3 and 6.

$6 \times 3 = (1 \times 3) + (5 \times 3)$

$6 \times 3 = 3 + 15$

$6 \times 3 = 18$

6 × 5
← 1 × 3
← 5 × 3

Can you use facts you know to find facts for 7 and 9?

Think

The array shows 7 rows of 8, or 7 × 8.

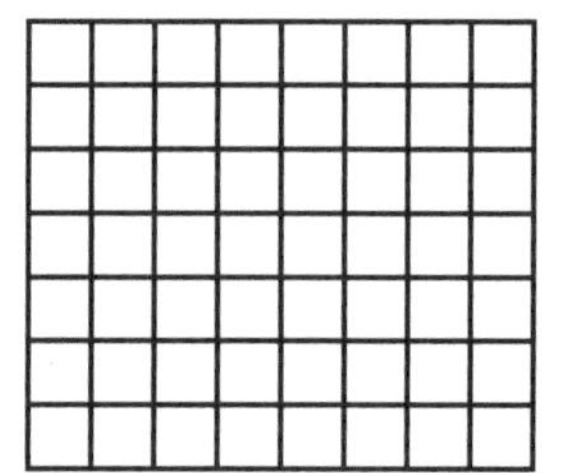

Connect

Use facts you know to find 7×8.

Think of 7 as $2 + 5$.

$7 \times 8 = (2 \times 8) + (5 \times 8)$

$7 \times 8 = 16 + 40$

$7 \times 8 = 56$

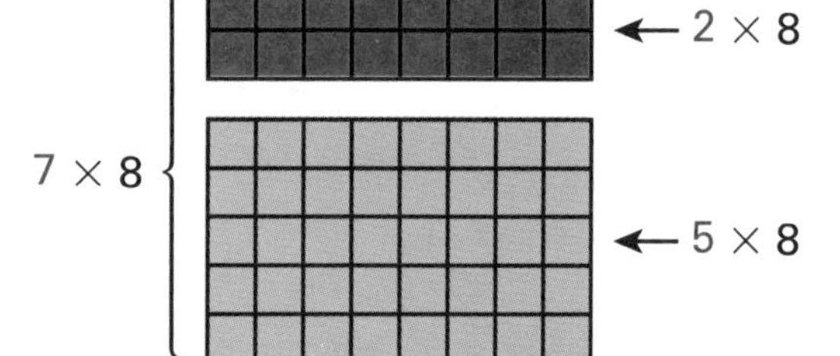

Because $7 = 2 + 5$, you can use 2s facts and 5s facts to find the 7s fact.

Let's Talk

How could you use a 3s fact and a 4s fact to show that $7 \times 8 = 56$?

Fill in the blanks. Solve the problem.

Tibet puts 6 stamps on each page of his album.
He fills 9 pages. How many stamps does Tibet use?

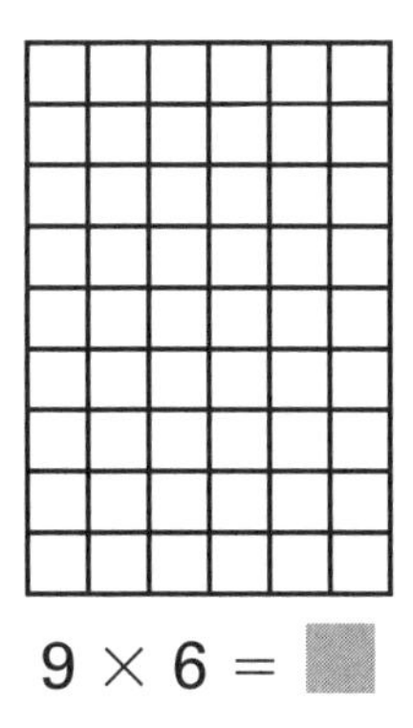

$9 \times 6 = \blacksquare$

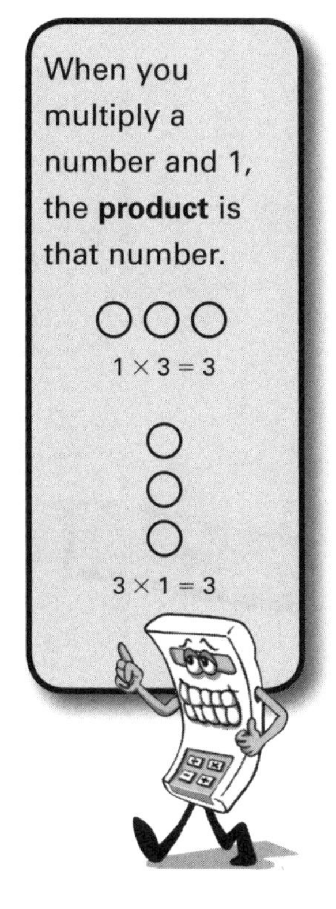

- Think of 9 as $5 + 4$.
- Use one color to shade ____ rows of 6 on the array.

  Use a different color to shade ____ rows of 6.
- $9 \times 6 = (\_\_\_\_ \times \_\_\_\_) + (\_\_\_\_ \times \_\_\_\_)$

  $9 \times 6 = \_\_\_\_ + \_\_\_\_$

  $9 \times 6 = \_\_\_\_$

Solution: Tibet uses ____ stamps.

Your Turn **Now, use what you know to solve this problem.**

2. Jolie has 7 different colors of crayons. She has 9 crayons of each color. How many crayons does Jolie have?

$7 \times 9 = (\_\_\_\_ \times 9) + (\_\_\_\_ \times 9)$

$7 \times 9 = \_\_\_\_ + \_\_\_\_$

$7 \times 9 = \_\_\_\_$

____ crayons

PART THREE: Choose the Right Answer

Solve the problem. Then read why each answer choice is correct or not correct.

Solve

Sally has a sheet with 6 rows of stickers.
There are 7 stickers in each row.
How many stickers does Sally have in all?

Ⓐ 13

Ⓑ 21

Ⓒ 42

Ⓓ 49

$6 \times 7 = \square$

Check

Check to see if you chose the correct answer.

One way to think of 6 is as 3 + 3.
Multiply 3 by 7 and 3 by 7. Then add.

$6 \times 7 = (3 \times 7) + (3 \times 7)$

$6 \times 7 = 21 + 21$

$6 \times 7 = 42$

So, the correct answer is Ⓒ.

Why are the other answer choices not correct?

Ⓐ 13	The numbers 6 and 7 should be multiplied, not added.
Ⓑ 21	The number 3 should be multiplied by 7 two times, not one time.
Ⓓ 49	There are 6 rows of stickers, not 7 rows.

Your Turn **Solve each problem. Use the hints to avoid mistakes.**

- Break up numbers so that you can use multiplication facts you know.
- After breaking up the number, be sure to add the products.

3. The singers in a choir stand in 3 rows. There are 9 singers in each row. How many singers are there in all?

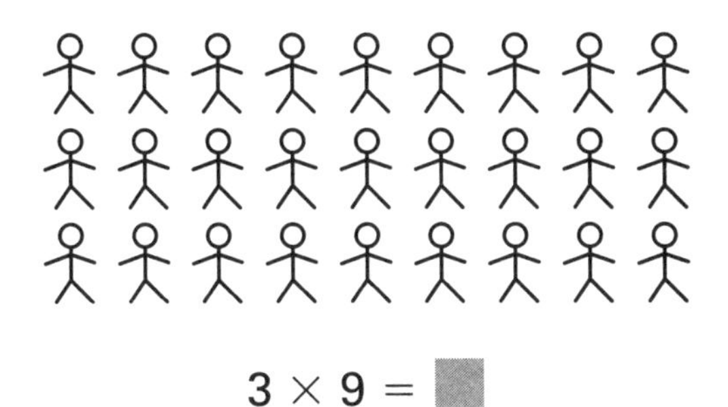

$3 \times 9 = \square$

Ⓐ 12

Ⓑ 18

Ⓒ 27

Ⓓ 36

4. What is 7×6?

Ⓐ 42

Ⓑ 36

Ⓒ 35

Ⓓ 30

5. Jeff puts his game pieces in 6 rows. He puts 6 pieces in each row. How many pieces does Jeff place in all?

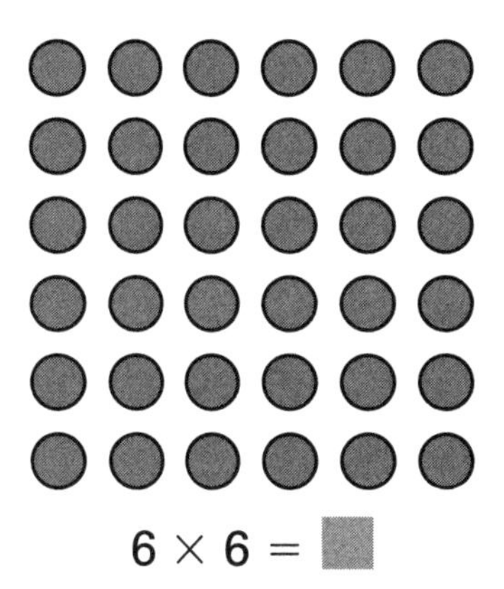

$6 \times 6 = \square$

Ⓐ 12

Ⓑ 30

Ⓒ 36

Ⓓ 42

6. What is 9×4?

Ⓐ 45

Ⓑ 36

Ⓒ 20

Ⓓ 13

Study the model. It is a good example of a written answer.

Student Model

Show

Carlos builds model planes from kits that are sold in boxes. He has 7 boxed kits. Each box has 8 model planes in it. How many planes in all does Carlos have?

Use pictures, words, or numbers to show your work.

7 groups of 8 = 7×8

$7 = 3 + 4$

$7 \times 8 = (3 \times 8) + (4 \times 8)$

$7 \times 8 = 24 + 32$

$7 \times 8 = 56$

☑ The student shows each step.

Solution: 56 model planes

☑ The student correctly answers the question asked.

Explain

Explain how you got your answer.

There are 7 equal groups with 8 planes in each group, or 7×8. I can think of 7 as the sum of 3 and 4. The product of 7×8 is $(3 \times 8) + (4 \times 8)$. $3 \times 8 = 24$, and $4 \times 8 = 32$. $24 + 32 = 56$, so Carlos has 56 model planes.

☑ The student gives important details about how to find the product.

☑ The student uses the math words *equal groups*, *sum*, and *product*.

Your Turn **Solve the problem. Use what you learned from the model.**

CHECKLIST

Did you . . .

- ☐ show each step?
- ☐ answer the question asked?
- ☐ give important details?
- ☐ use math words?

7. Students are sitting in 6 rows watching a puppet show. There are 9 students in each row. How many students are watching the puppet show in all?

   Use pictures, words, or numbers to show your work.

Solution: ____ students

Explain how you got your answer.

____

____

____

____

____

As you solve multiplication problems, remember to
- break up numbers so you can use facts you know.
- multiply each pair of numbers first. Then add the products.

Solve each problem.

8. Postcards come in packages of 6. Mandy buys 3 packages of postcards. How many postcards does Mandy buy in all?

$$3 \times 6 = \blacksquare$$

Ⓐ 9
Ⓑ 12
Ⓒ 15
Ⓓ 18

9. Kennie buys 7 packages of marbles. Each package has 4 marbles in it. Which is another way to find 7×4?

Ⓐ $(3 \times 4) + (3 \times 4)$
Ⓑ $(4 + 4) \times (3 + 4)$
Ⓒ $(4 \times 4) + (3 \times 4)$
Ⓓ $(4 \times 4) \times (3 \times 4)$

10. Students are standing in 6 rows to get their picture taken. There are 6 students in each row. How many students are getting their picture taken?

$$6 \times 6 = \blacksquare$$

Ⓐ 12
Ⓑ 18
Ⓒ 36
Ⓓ 42

11. What is 9×3?

Ⓐ 12
Ⓑ 18
Ⓒ 27
Ⓓ 36

12. The clerk in a card shop puts 4 greeting cards in each of 6 rows. Which shows how to find the total number of cards?

Ⓐ $(4 + 4) \times (2 + 4)$
Ⓑ $(3 \times 4) + (1 \times 4)$
Ⓒ $(4 \times 4) \times (2 \times 4)$
Ⓓ $(4 \times 4) + (2 \times 4)$

13. A bakery displays a tray of muffins. The tray has 7 rows with 3 muffins in each row. How many muffins are on the tray in all?

Ⓐ 10

Ⓑ 18

Ⓒ 21

Ⓓ 28

14. Ana is planting a flower garden. She plants 9 rows with 4 daisies in each row. How many daisies did she plant in all?

Write a number sentence that shows another way to find 9×4. Then find the answer.

Number sentence:

____

Solution: _____ daisies

15. Cars are parked in 7 rows in the school parking lot. Each row has 7 cars. How many cars are in the parking lot in all?

Use pictures, words, or numbers to show your work.

Solution: _____ cars

Explain how you found your answer.

____

____

____

____

____

Lesson 6 DIVISION CONCEPTS

PART ONE: Learn About Equal Sharing and Division

How can sharing equally help you understand division?

Explore

Multiplication is a way to join **equal groups** to find a total.

3	×	4	=	12
↑		↑		↑
number of groups		number in each group		total amount

Suppose you know the number of groups and the total amount.

How can you find the number in each group?

Think

Division is a way to separate an amount into equal groups.

15 ÷ 5 = ▇ — How many will be in each group?

How many counters are there in all? 15

How many groups are there? 5

Connect

1. To **divide** 15 into 5 equal groups, put one counter in each of the 5 groups.	
2. Continue until all of the counters have been shared equally among the groups.	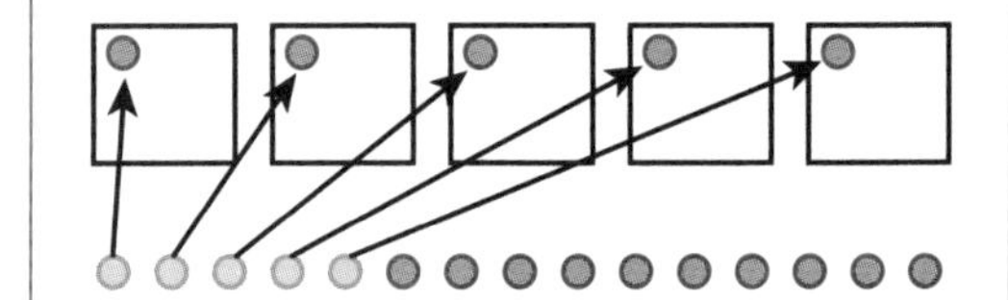

There are 3 counters in each group. So, 15 ÷ 5 = 3.

Let's Talk

Why do you need to put the counters one by one into each group?

Fill in the blanks. Solve the problem.

Thomas has 20 crayons. He puts the same number of crayons in each of 4 boxes. How many crayons are in each box?

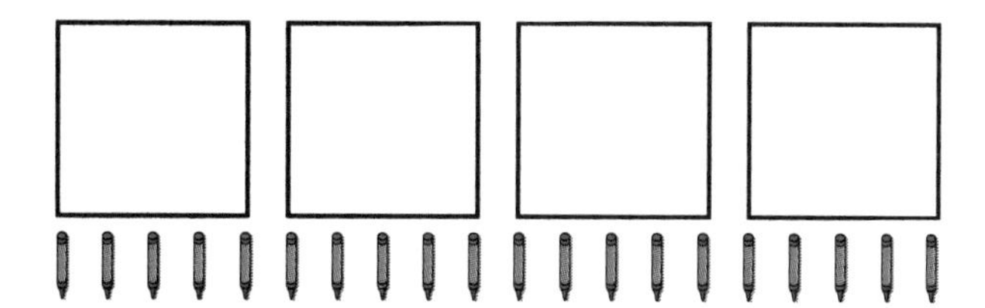

- How many crayons are there in all? _____

  How many boxes, or groups, are there? _____

- Put one crayon in each group until there are no crayons left.

  How many crayons are in each group? _____

- Write a division sentence that shows how many are in each group. _____ ÷ _____ = _____

Solution: There are _______ crayons in each box.

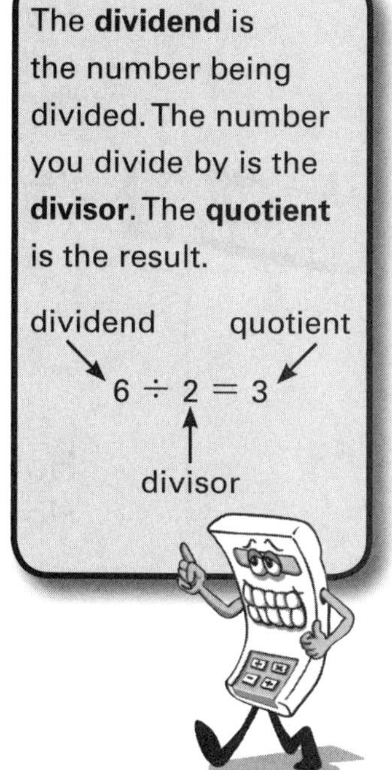

Your Turn **Now, use what you know to solve this problem.**

1. Tamara is putting 14 apples in bags. She puts the same number of apples in each of 7 bags. How many apples are in each bag? Use the drawing to help you find the answer.

$14 \div 7 = \square$

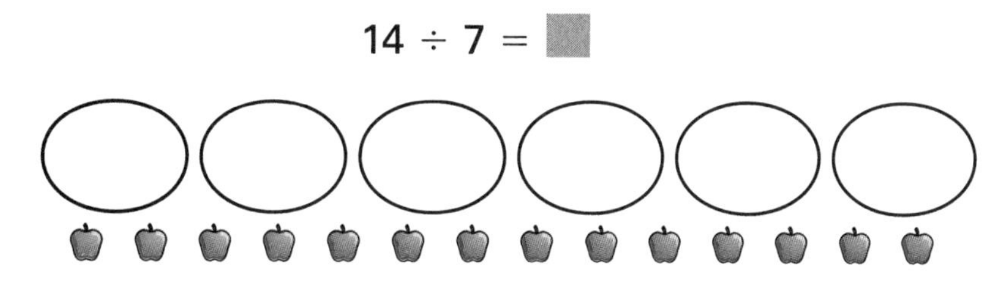

Ⓐ 1

Ⓑ 2

Ⓒ 7

Ⓓ 21

How can subtracting equal groups help you understand division?

Explore

You can use division to find the number in each group.

8	÷	4	=	2
total amount		number of groups		number in each group

Suppose you know the number in each group and the total amount.

How can you find the number of groups?

Think

$12 \div 4 = \square$

How many groups of 4 are there in 12?

How many counters are there in all? 12

How many counters are in each group? 4

Connect

Repeated subtraction can help you understand division.
Start with 12 counters. Subtract 4 counters.
Keep subtracting 4 counters until you reach zero.
Count the number of times you subtracted 4.

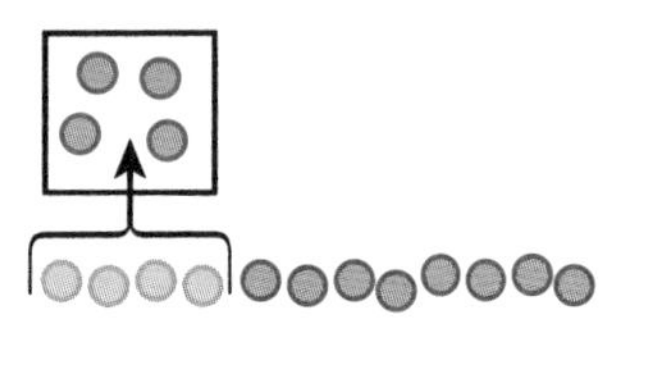

$12 - 4 = 8$
1

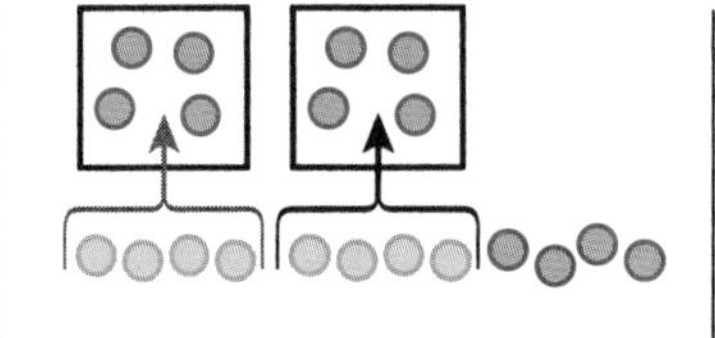

$8 - 4 = 4$
2

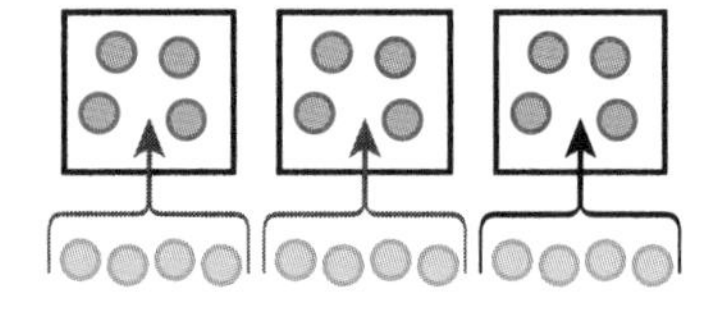

$4 - 4 = 0$
3

You subtract 4 three times. $12 - 4 - 4 - 4 = 0$.
So, $12 \div 4 = 3$.

Let's Talk

In everyday life, when might you use repeated subtraction to divide? Think of two or three examples.

Fill in the blanks. Solve the problem.

Marco has 30 water balloons. He needs to put 5 balloons in each bucket. How many buckets does Marco need?

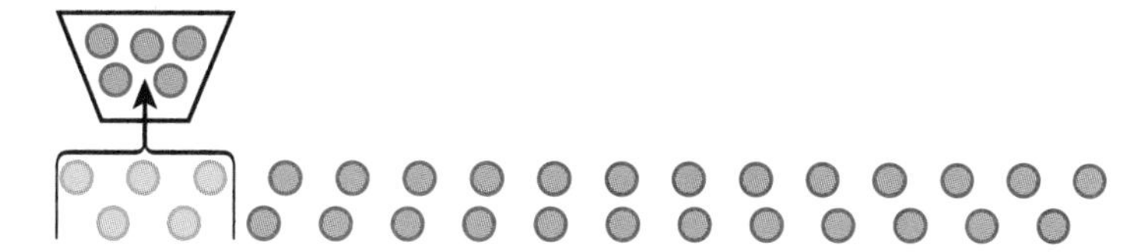

- How many water balloons are there in all? ____

  How many balloons are in each bucket? ____

- Use repeated subtraction to find the number of buckets.

  Subtract 5 from 30 until you get zero.

  30 − ____ = ____ 25 − ____ = ____ 20 − ____ = ____

  15 − ____ = ____ 10 − ____ = ____ 5 − ____ = ____

- You subtracted 5 from 30 six times.

  30 − ____ − ____ − ____ − ____ − ____ − ____ = 0

  So, 30 ÷ 5 = ____.

Solution: Marco needs ______ buckets of balloons.

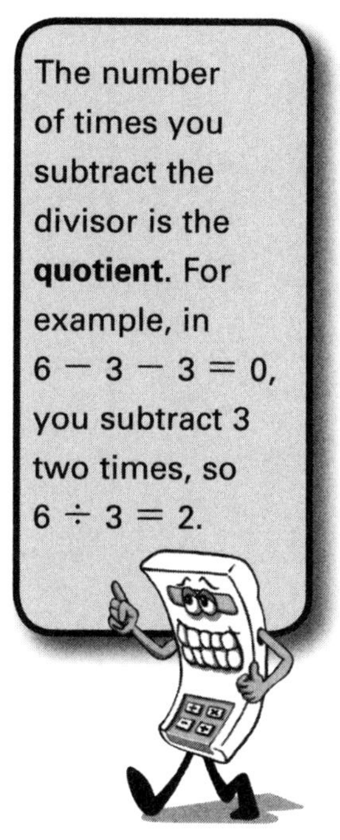

Your Turn **Now, use what you know to solve this problem.**

2. Bobbi is planting 10 tomato seeds in pots.
   She wants to plant 2 seeds in each pot.
   How many pots does she need?
   Use the drawing to help you find the answer.

   10 ÷ 2 = ■

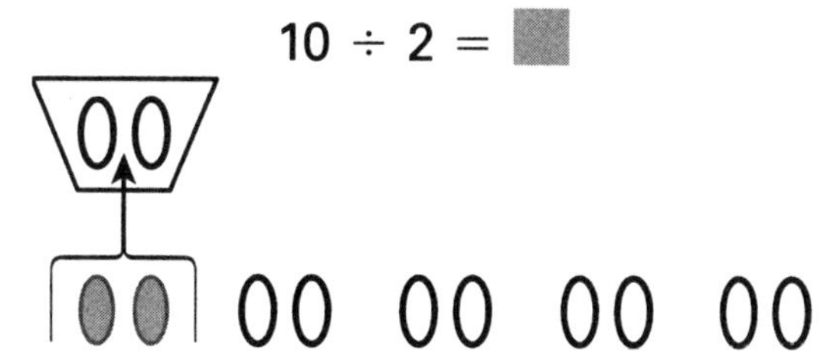

____ pots

Solve the problem. Then read why each answer choice is correct or not correct.

Solve

Michael has 18 apples. He divides the apples equally among 3 bowls. How many apples are in each bowl?

$18 \div 3 = \blacksquare$

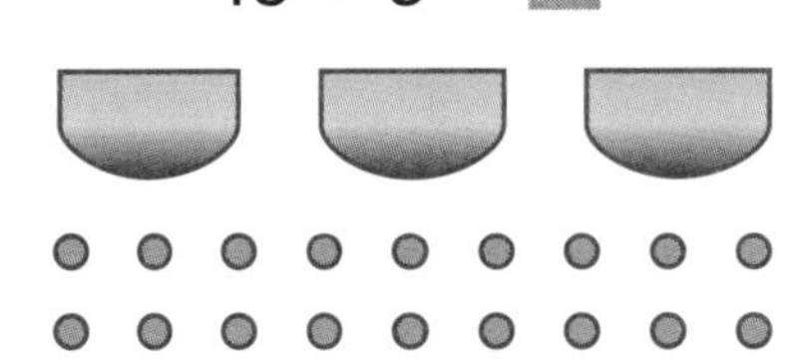

Ⓐ 21

Ⓑ 15

Ⓒ 6

Ⓓ 3

Check

Check to see if you chose the correct answer.

There are 18 apples in all.
The apples are divided equally into 3 bowls.

$18 \div 3 = 6$

There are 6 apples in each bowl.

So, the correct answer is Ⓒ.

Why are the other answer choices not correct?

Ⓐ 21	This is the sum of 18 and 3.
Ⓑ 15	This is the difference between 18 and 3.
Ⓓ 3	The number in each group should be found, not the number of groups.

Your Turn **Solve each problem. Use the hints to avoid mistakes.**

- Draw pictures to help you find the number of groups or the number in each group.
- Be sure to put the same number of items in each group when finding the number in each group.
- Keep subtracting the correct amount from the total when finding the number of groups.

3. Mr. Beste has 24 colored pencils. He gives the same number of pencils to 6 of his students. How many colored pencils does each student get?

$24 \div 6 = \blacksquare$

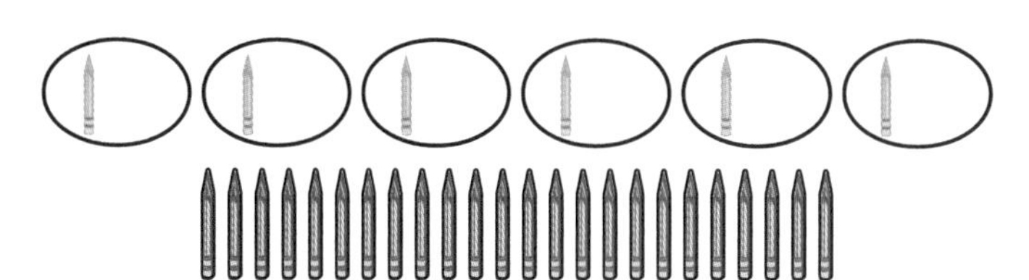

Ⓐ 4 Ⓑ 6 Ⓒ 18 Ⓓ 24

4. Lila is putting 20 flowers in vases. She wants to put 4 flowers in each vase. How many vases does she need?

$20 \div 4 = \blacksquare$

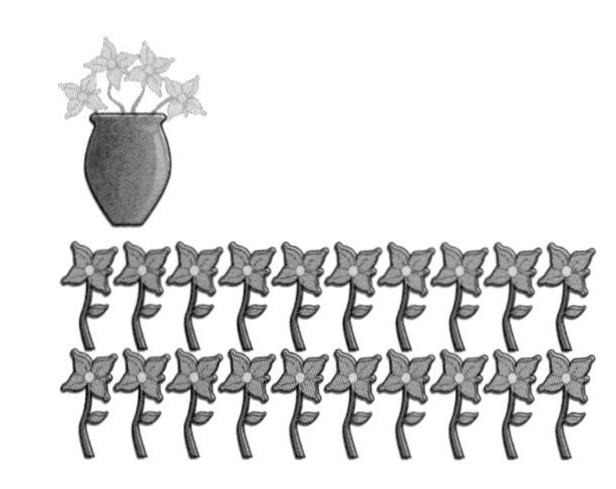

Ⓐ 4 Ⓑ 5 Ⓒ 16 Ⓓ 24

5. Monica is putting 21 baseball cards in a book. She puts the same number of cards on 3 pages of the book. How many cards does she put on each page?

$21 \div 3 = \blacksquare$

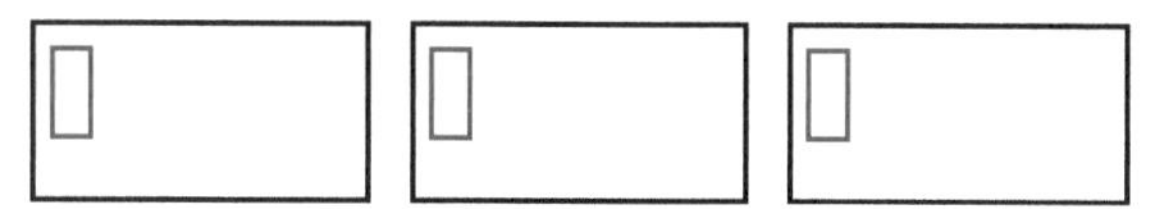

Ⓐ 21 Ⓑ 18 Ⓒ 7 Ⓓ 6

6. Jorge has 9 toy cars. He wants to put 3 cars in each basket. How many baskets does he need?

$9 \div 3 = \blacksquare$

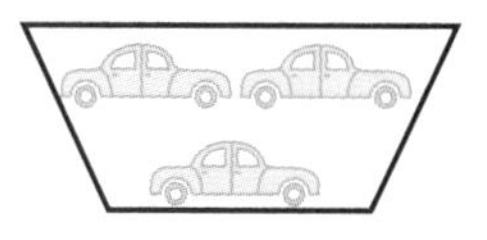

Ⓐ 12 Ⓑ 9 Ⓒ 6 Ⓓ 3

Study the model. It is a good example of a written answer.

Student Model

Show

Mrs. Rios is tying 20 balloons to weights for a party. She wants to tie 5 balloons to each weight. How many weights does Mrs. Rios need?

Use pictures, words, or numbers to show your work.

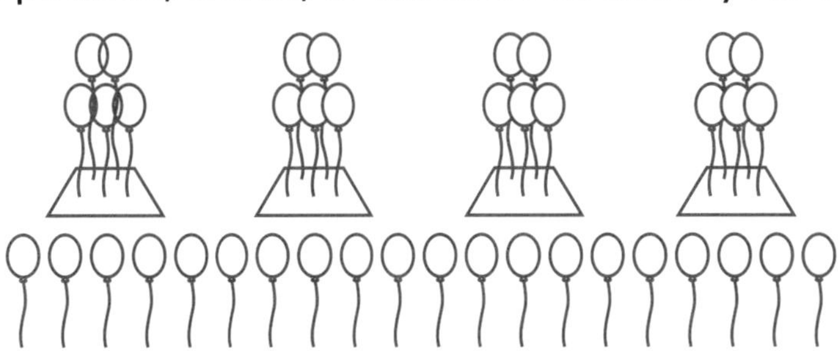

☑ The student shows each step.

20 balloons in all

5 balloons on each weight

$20 - 5 - 5 - 5 - 5 = 0$

$20 \div 5 = 4$

Solution: 4 weights

☑ The student correctly answers the question asked.

Explain

Explain how you got your answer.

There are 20 balloons in all. The balloons need to be divided into equal groups, with 5 balloons in each group. I used repeated subtraction to subtract 5 from 20 until I got zero. I subtracted 5 four times, so $20 \div 5 = 4$. Mrs. Rios needs 4 weights.

☑ The student gives important details about how to find the quotient.

☑ The student uses the math words *divide*, *equal groups*, and *repeated subtraction*.

Your Turn **Solve the problem. Use what you learned from the model.**

7. A librarian is putting 24 books on shelves. He wants to put the same number of books on each shelf. Each shelf can fit 8 books. How many shelves does the librarian need?

   Use pictures, words, or numbers to show your work.

CHECKLIST

Did you . . .

- ☐ show each step?
- ☐ answer the question asked?
- ☐ give important details?
- ☐ use math words?

Solution: _______ shelves

Explain how you got your answer.

____

____

____

____

____

____

As you solve division problems, you may want to
- draw pictures to show equal groups.
- use repeated subtraction to check your work.

Solve each problem.

8. There are 3 dogs. The dogs are going to share 18 bones equally. How many bones will each dog get?

$18 \div 3 = \blacksquare$

Ⓐ 21
Ⓑ 18
Ⓒ 16
Ⓓ 6

9. Ava is putting away 12 sweaters. She wants to put 3 sweaters in each drawer. How many drawers does Ava need?

$12 \div 3 = \blacksquare$

Ⓐ 4
Ⓑ 6
Ⓒ 12
Ⓓ 15

10. Troy has 12 baseball caps. He wants to hang 6 caps on each hook.

Which number sentence can be used to find how many hooks Troy needs?

Ⓐ $12 - 6 - 6 - 6 = \blacksquare$
Ⓑ $12 - 6 - 6 = \blacksquare$
Ⓒ $12 - 6 = \blacksquare$
Ⓓ $12 \div 6 \div 6 = \blacksquare$

11. While on vacation, Sam bought 8 postcards. He sent the same number of postcards to each of his 4 cousins. How many postcards did each cousin get?

$8 \div 4 = \blacksquare$

Ⓐ 2
Ⓑ 4
Ⓒ 8
Ⓓ 12

12. Chloe picked up 32 seashells at the beach. She put the same number of seashells in each of 4 buckets. How many seashells were in each bucket?

Ⓐ 2
Ⓑ 8
Ⓒ 28
Ⓓ 36

13. Laura's mom bought 15 goldfish to put in fish tanks. Each tank can hold 5 fish. How many tanks does she need?

Ⓐ 3
Ⓑ 5
Ⓒ 15
Ⓓ 20

14. A pet store has 24 hamsters. The shop owner wants to put 4 hamsters in a cage. How many cages does the owner need for all the hamsters?

$$24 \div 4 = \blacksquare$$

Write a subtraction sentence to help you divide. Then write the answer.

____

______ cages

15. Nicholas divided his 36 playing cards into 6 equal stacks. How many cards are in each stack?

Use pictures, words, or numbers to show your work.

Solution: ______ cards

Explain how you found your answer.

____

____

____

____

____

Lesson 7 FACT FAMILIES

PART ONE: Learn About Multiplication and Division Fact Families

What are fact families?

Explore

You have used **arrays** to help you understand multiplication.

2 groups of 5

$2 \times 5 = 10$

How can an array show that multiplication and division facts are related?

Think

You can look at an array two ways.

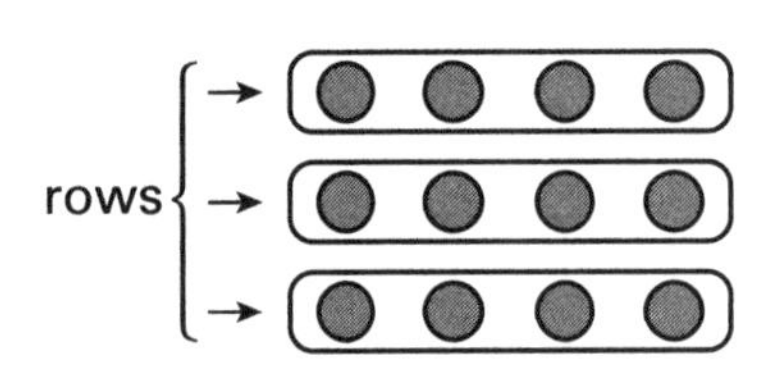

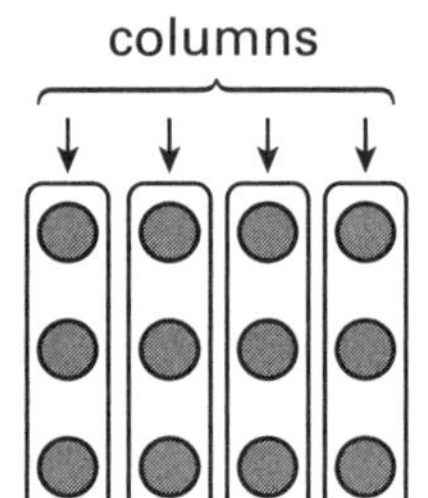

3 groups of 4

4 groups of 3

Connect

You can write multiplication and division sentences for the array.

$3 \times 4 = 12$ $12 \div 3 = 4$

$4 \times 3 = 12$ $12 \div 4 = 3$

These four number sentences make up a **fact family**.
Each number sentence uses the same numbers: 3, 4, and 12.

Let's Talk

Find the other facts in the fact family that includes $3 \times 3 = 9$.
What do you discover about the fact family?
Find other fact families like this one.

Fill in the blanks. Solve the problem.

What is the fact family for this array?

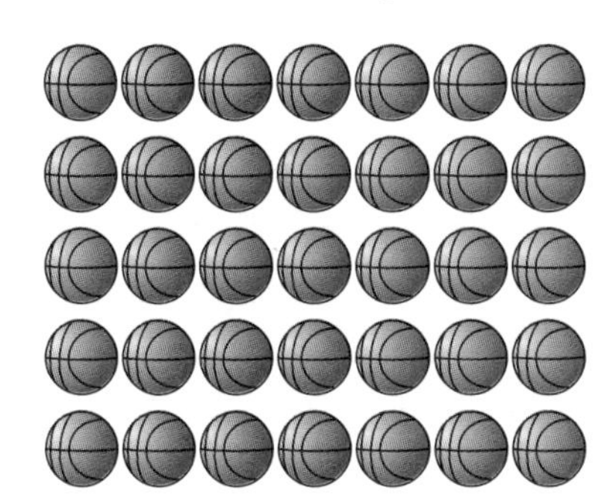

In multiplication the total is the **product**. The number of groups and the number in each group are the **factors**.
factor × factor = product

- How many rows are there? _____

  How many basketballs are in each row? _____

- How many columns are there? _____

  How many basketballs are in each column? _____

- How many basketballs are there in all? _____

- Write two multiplication sentences for the array.

  _____ × _____ = _____ and _____ × _____ = _____

- Write two division sentences for the array.

  _____ ÷ _____ = _____ and _____ ÷ _____ = _____

Solution: _____ × _____ = _____   _____ ÷ _____ = _____

_____ × _____ = _____   _____ ÷ _____ = _____

Your Turn **Now, use what you know to solve this problem.**

1. Which number sentence is part of the fact family for this array?

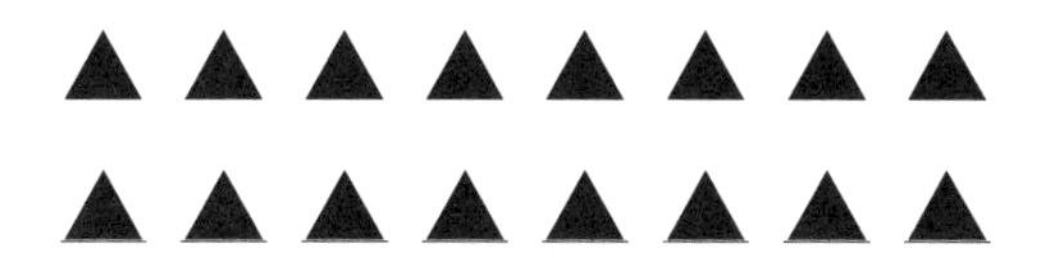

Ⓐ $8 + 2 = 10$ Ⓒ $8 \div 2 = 4$

Ⓑ $8 \times 2 = 16$ Ⓓ $16 \div 4 = 4$

How can you use fact families to find missing numbers in number sentences?

Explore

Fact families show how multiplication and division facts are related.

Fact family for 3, 6, and 18

$3 \times 6 = 18$ $18 \div 3 = 6$

$6 \times 3 = 18$ $18 \div 6 = 3$

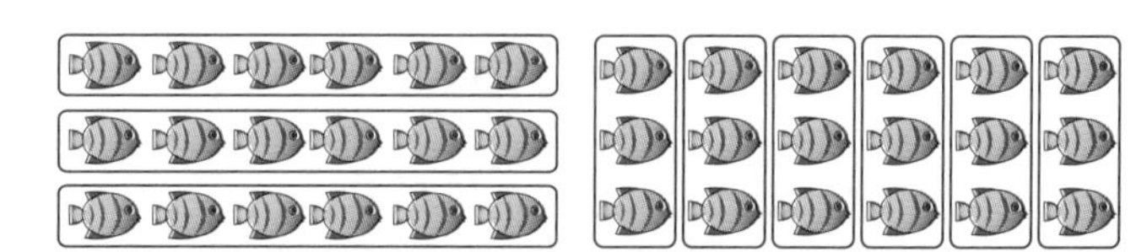

How can you use related facts to find missing numbers?

Think

$27 \div 3 = \square$

This problem can mean →
divide 27 into 3 equal groups.

This problem can also mean →
divide 27 into equal groups of 3.

Connect

The multiplication sentences and division sentences in a fact family use the same numbers.

The array shows $3 \times 9 = 27$ and $9 \times 3 = 27$.

Use these facts to find the missing number in the division sentence.
$27 \div 3 = \boxed{9}$

Let's Talk

In a fact family, what is the same and what is different about the multiplication sentences? What is the same and what is different about the division sentences?

Fill in the blanks. Solve the problem.

What is the missing number in 40 ÷ ▒ = 5.
Use the array to help you.

In division the total is the **dividend.** You can use either the number of groups or the number in each group as the **divisor.** The answer is the **quotient.**
dividend ÷ divisor = quotient

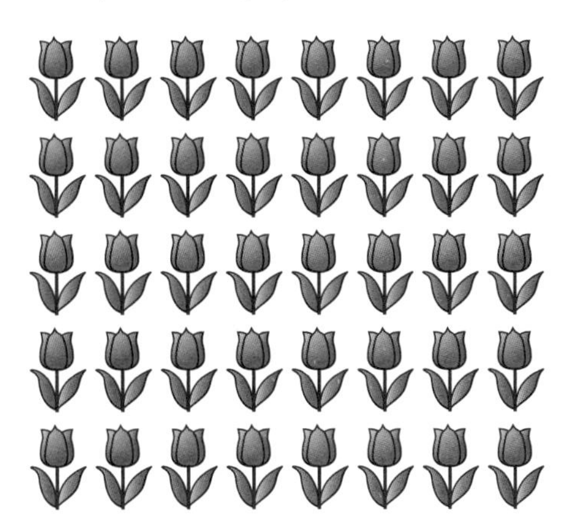

- This problem can mean divide _____ into _____ equal groups.
  This problem can also mean divide _____ into equal groups of _____.
- Write the multiplication facts for the array.
  _____ × _____ = _____ and _____ × _____ = _____
- Write the division facts for the array.
  _____ ÷ _____ = _____ and _____ ÷ _____ = _____

Solution: The missing number is _____.

Now, use what you know to solve this problem.

2. Find the fact family for the array. Then use the fact family to find the missing number.

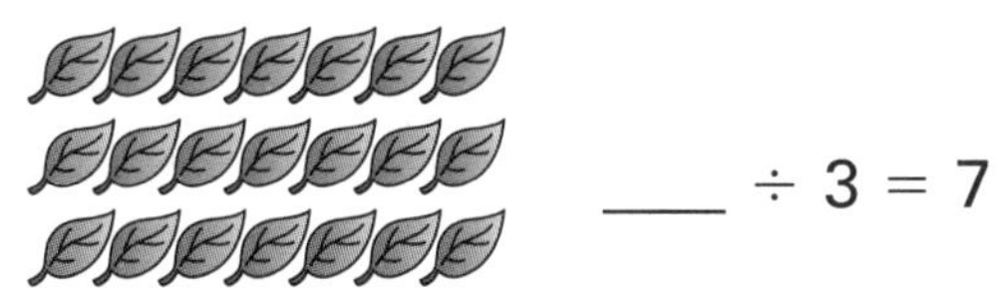

____ ÷ 3 = 7

_____ × _____ = _____ _____ ÷ _____ = _____

_____ × _____ = _____ _____ ÷ _____ = _____

Solve the problem. Then read why each answer choice is correct or not correct.

Solve

Look at the array.

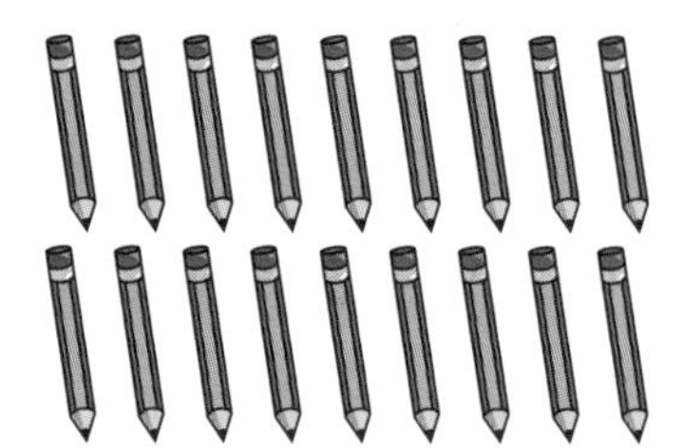

Which number sentence is in the fact family shown by the array?

Ⓐ $2 \times 9 = 18$

Ⓑ $18 \div 3 = 6$

Ⓒ $9 - 2 = 7$

Ⓓ $9 + 2 = 11$

Check

Check to see if you chose the correct answer.

There are 2 rows of 9 pencils.
2 groups of 9 is the same as 2×9.
$2 \times 9 = 18$

So, the correct answer is Ⓐ.

Why are the other answer choices not correct?

Ⓑ $18 \div 3 = 6$	The array shows 18 divided into 2 rows, not 3 or 6 rows.
Ⓒ $9 - 2 = 7$	The array shows 2 rows, or groups, of 9, not “2 less than 9.”
Ⓓ $9 + 2 = 11$	The array shows 2 rows, or groups, of 9, not “2 more than 9.”

Your Turn **Solve each problem. Use the hints to avoid mistakes.**

- Use all the same numbers in each sentence of a fact family.
- Carefully count the rows and the items in each row of an array.

3. Which number sentence is in the fact family shown by the array?

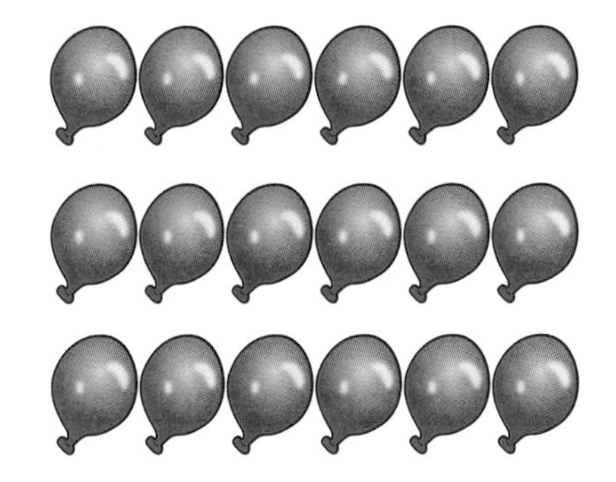

Ⓐ $6 \times 6 = 36$

Ⓑ $18 \div 3 = 6$

Ⓒ $18 \div 2 = 9$

Ⓓ $2 \times 9 = 18$

4. What is the missing number?

$3 \times \square = 27$

Ⓐ 3

Ⓑ 6

Ⓒ 9

Ⓓ 24

5. Which number sentence is in the fact family shown by the array?

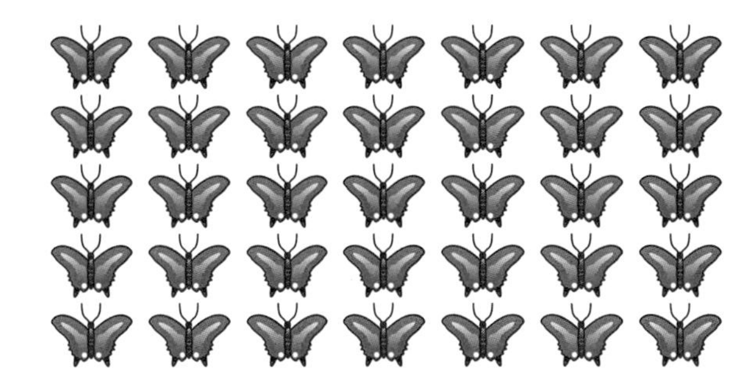

Ⓐ $7 \times 5 = 35$

Ⓑ $25 \div 5 = 5$

Ⓒ $3 \times 7 = 21$

Ⓓ $40 \div 5 = 8$

6. Which two number sentences are in the same fact family?

Ⓐ $6 \times 7 = 42$ and $42 - 7 = 35$

Ⓑ $7 \times 6 = 42$ and $42 \div 6 = 7$

Ⓒ $42 \div 6 = 7$ and $6 + 7 = 13$

Ⓓ $63 \div 7 = 9$ and $7 \times 6 = 42$

Study the model. It is a good example of a written answer.

Student Model

Show

A store sells bottles of water arranged as shown.

What numbers are in the fact family shown by the array? Use pictures, words, or numbers to show your work.

2 groups of 10 or 10 groups of 2
20 bottles in all
$2 \times 10 = 20$ $20 \div 2 = 10$
$10 \times 2 = 20$ $20 \div 10 = 2$

Solution: The numbers in the fact family are 2, 10, and 20.

☑ The student shows each step.

☑ The student correctly answers the question asked.

Explain

Explain how you got your answer.

The array shows 2 groups of 10 or 10 groups of 2. There are 20 water bottles in all. I wrote the fact family for the array: $2 \times 10 = 20$, $10 \times 2 = 20$, $20 \div 2 = 10$, and $20 \div 10 = 2$. So, the numbers in the fact family are 2, 10, and 20.

☑ The student gives important details about how to find the numbers in the fact family.

☑ The student uses the math words *array* and *fact family.*

Your Turn — Solve the problem. Use what you learned from the model.

CHECKLIST

Did you . . .

- ☐ show each step?
- ☐ answer the question asked?
- ☐ give important details?
- ☐ use math words?

7. Mr. Sanders has pages of scrapbooking letters.

A A A A A
A A A A A
A A A A A
A A A A A
A A A A A
A A A A A

What numbers are in the fact family shown by the array of letters?

Use pictures, words, or numbers to show your work.

Solution: The numbers in the fact family are _______, _______, and _______.

Explain how you got your answer.

____

____

____

____

____

As you solve fact-family problems, you may want to:

- use an array to find the numbers in a fact family.
- multiply or divide to check your answer.

Solve each problem.

8. Which number sentence is in the fact family shown by this array?

Ⓐ $2 \times 4 = 8$

Ⓑ $10 \times 2 = 20$

Ⓒ $12 \div 2 = 6$

Ⓓ $10 \div 2 = 5$

9. Which number sentence is in the same fact family as $5 \times 9 = 45$?

Ⓐ $6 \times 9 = 54$

Ⓑ $45 - 9 = 36$

Ⓒ $45 \div 9 = 5$

Ⓓ $9 - 5 = 4$

10. Which number sentence can help you find the missing number?

$$10 \times \square = 40$$

Ⓐ $40 \div 10 = 4$

Ⓑ $40 \div 8 = 5$

Ⓒ $10 \div 2 = 5$

Ⓓ $10 \times 40 = 400$

11. Katherine tells her teacher that 4, 6, and 28 are in the same fact family. The teacher says that is incorrect. What should Katherine change to make her fact family correct?

Ⓐ Use 24 instead of 28.

Ⓑ Use 8 instead of 6.

Ⓒ Use 7 instead of 4.

Ⓓ Use 30 instead of 28.

12. What is the missing number?

$36 \div \blacksquare = 9$

Ⓐ 3

Ⓑ 4

Ⓒ 6

Ⓓ 27

13. Which array could you use to show the fact family for 2, 4, and 8?

Ⓐ 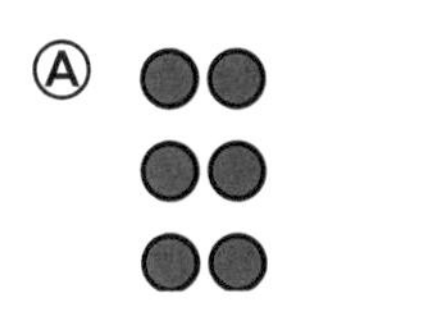

Ⓒ 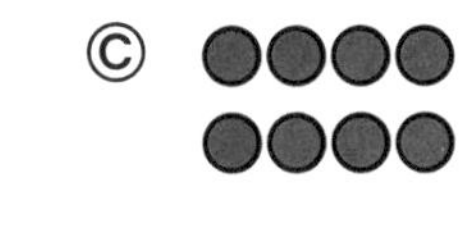

Ⓑ 

Ⓓ 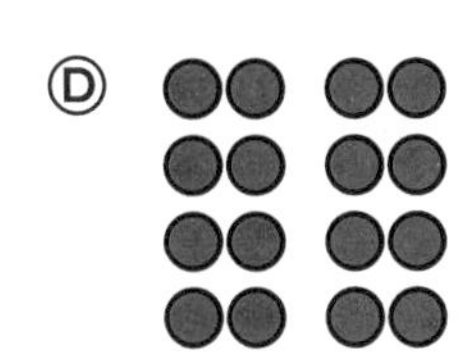

14. Write the number sentences in the fact family shown by the array.

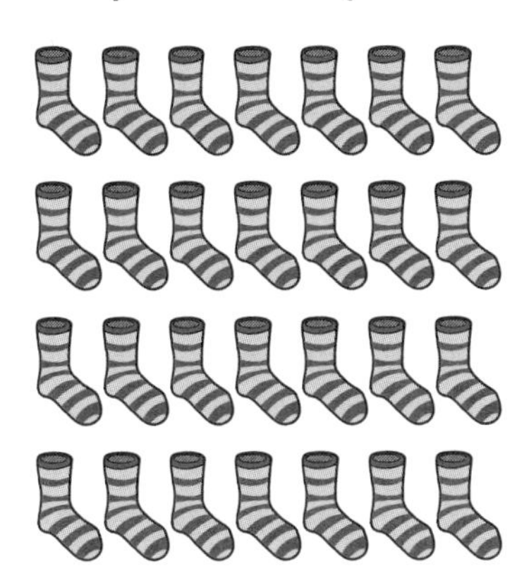

_______ × _______ = _______

_______ × _______ = _______

_______ ÷ _______ = _______

_______ ÷ _______ = _______

15. Tiara arranges her shells in an array as shown. What numbers are in the fact family shown by the array of shells?

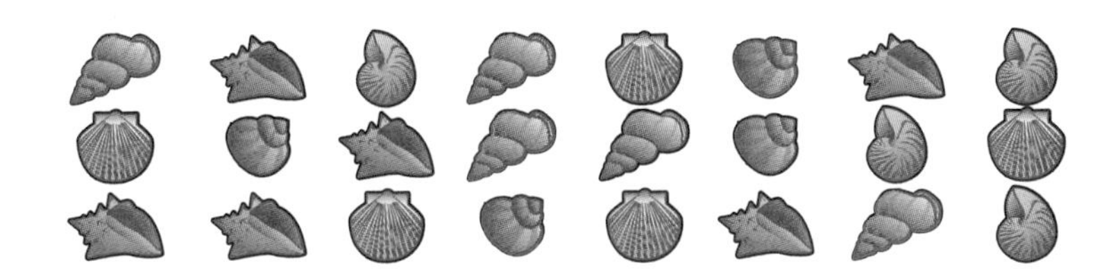

Use pictures, words, or numbers to show your work.

Solution: The numbers in the fact family are _______, _______, and _______.

Explain how you got your answer.

____

____

____

Lesson 8 FRACTION CONCEPTS

PART ONE: Learn About Fractions as Parts of a Whole

What are fractions?

Explore

You can divide an amount into equal groups.

What happens when you divide a whole into equal parts?

12 divided into 3 equal groups with 4 in each group

$12 \div 3 = 4$

Think

This model shows a whole divided into smaller parts.

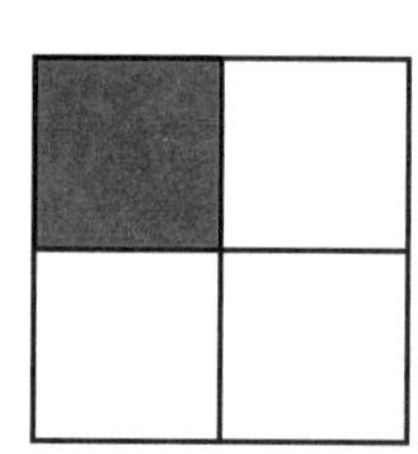

Are the parts the same size? yes

How many total parts are there? 4

How many parts are shaded? 1

Connect

A **fraction** is a number that names part of a whole that has been divided into equal parts.

1 of 4 equal parts are shaded on the model.

The model shows the fraction $\frac{1}{4}$.

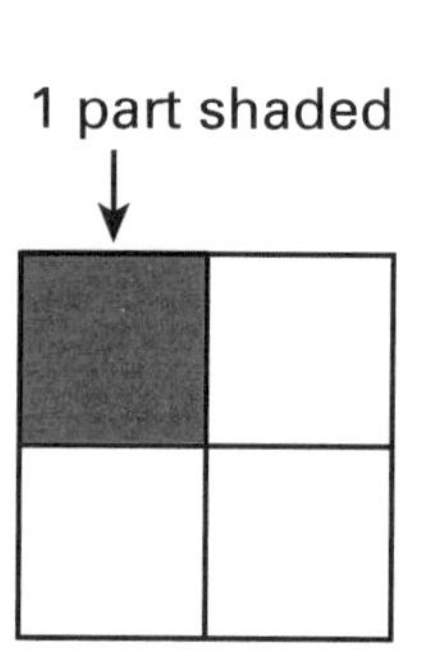

1 ← **numerator:** number of shaded parts

4 ← **denominator:** total number of equal parts in the whole

Read $\frac{1}{4}$ as "one fourth."

Let's Talk

Do both of these models show $\frac{1}{4}$? Why or why not?

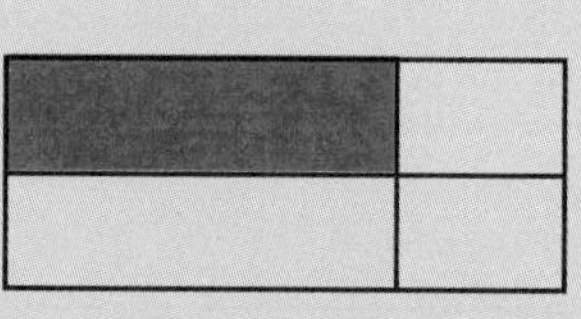

Fill in the blanks. Solve the problem.

What fraction does the model show?

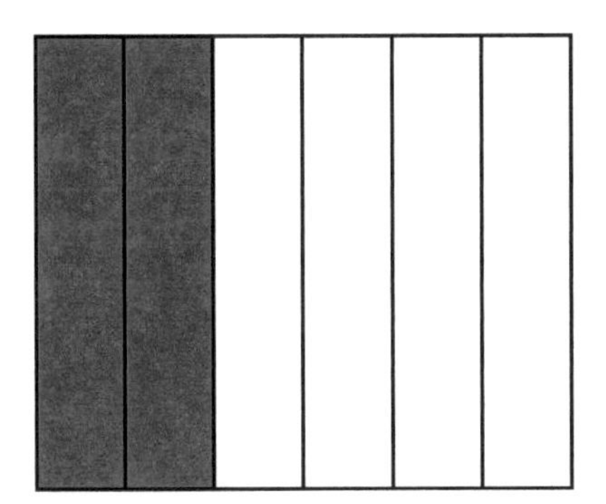

A group of items can be thought of as a whole.

There are 5 marbles, and 3 marbles are red. So, $\frac{3}{5}$ of the marbles are red.

- Are the parts of the model the same size? _____
- Find the denominator.
  How many total parts are there? _____
- Find the numerator.
  How many parts are shaded? _____
- Write the fraction. 

Solution: The model shows $\frac{\square}{\square}$.

Your Turn **Now, use what you know to solve this problem.**

1. Which fraction does the model show?

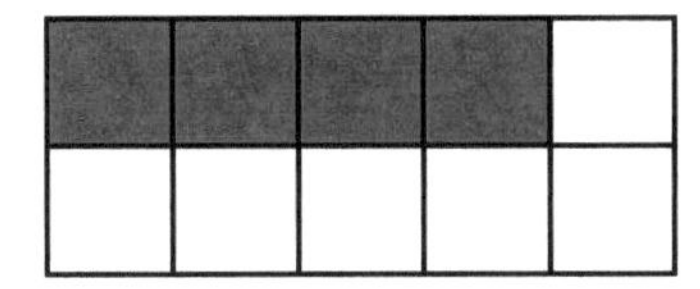

Ⓐ $\frac{4}{5}$ Ⓒ $\frac{4}{10}$

Ⓑ $\frac{4}{6}$ Ⓓ $\frac{6}{10}$

How can you use a number line to show a fraction?

Explore

You can show a fraction by shading equal parts of a whole.

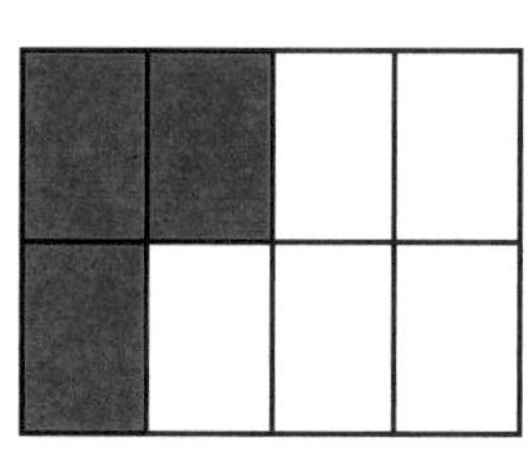

three eighths = $\frac{3}{8}$ ← shaded parts / ← total parts

What is another way to show a fraction?

Think

A **number line** can also show a fraction.

On this number line, the distance from 0 to 1 shows one whole.

$\frac{0}{4}$ $\frac{1}{4}$ $\frac{2}{4}$ $\frac{3}{4}$ $\frac{4}{4}$

0 1

How many parts is the whole divided into? 4

Are the parts equal? yes

How many parts away from 0 is the point? 3

Connect

The whole is divided into 4 equal parts, or fourths.

Each part is one fourth.

The point is 3 fourths away from 0.

The number line shows the fraction $\frac{3}{4}$.

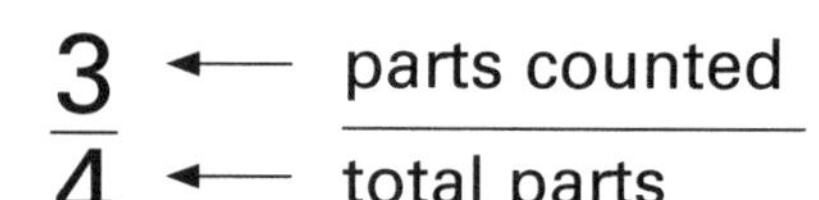

$\frac{3}{4}$ ← parts counted / ← total parts

Let's Talk

How many equal parts are there between 0 and 1 on this number line?

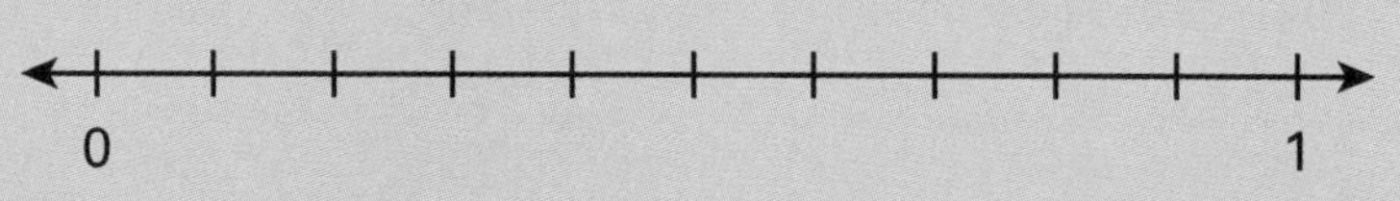

What fractions can you show on the number line?

Fill in the blanks. Solve the problem.

What fraction does the point on the number line show?

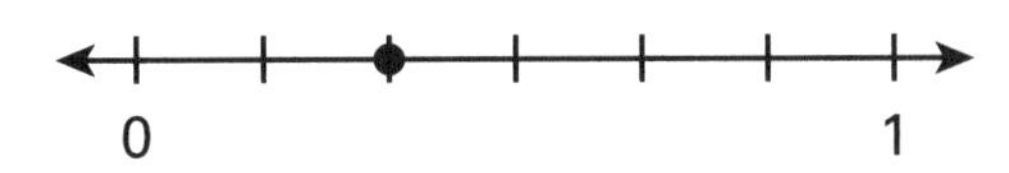

- Find the denominator.
  Count the number of equal parts in one whole.

  On the number line, the distance between 0 and 1

  is divided into _____ equal parts.

  Each part is one ___________.

- Find the numerator.
  Look at the point on the number line.

  How many parts away from 0 is the point? _____

  The point is _____ sixths away from 0.

- Write the fraction. $\frac{\square}{\square}$

Solution: The point shows the fraction $\frac{\square}{\square}$.

The denominator tells the number of equal parts. The numerator tells the distance from 0 on a number line.

Now, use what you know to solve this problem.

2. Draw a number line that shows one whole divided into 5 equal parts. Label 0 and 1. Then place a point on the number line to show the fraction $\frac{3}{5}$.

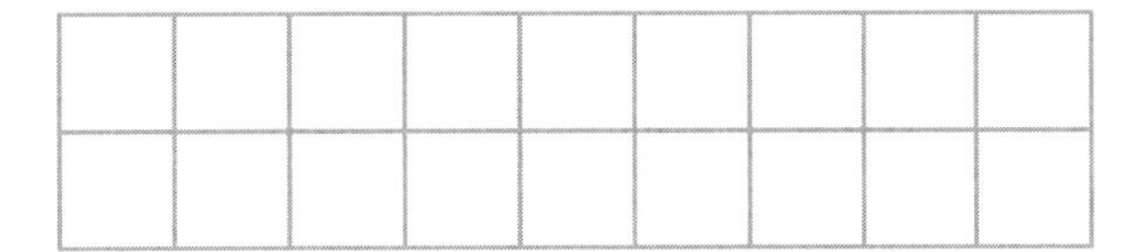

Solve the problem. Then read why each answer choice is correct or not correct.

Solve

Latoya has painted only part of her fence.

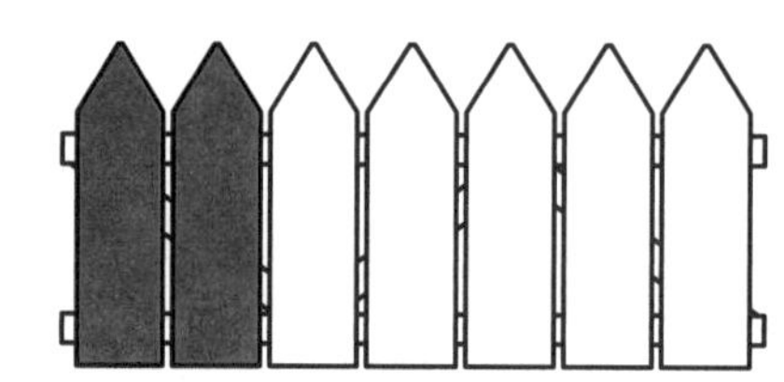

Which fraction tells how much of her fence she painted?

Ⓐ $\frac{7}{2}$

Ⓑ $\frac{2}{5}$

Ⓒ $\frac{2}{7}$

Ⓓ $\frac{5}{7}$

Check

Check to see if you chose the correct answer.

The parts are equal in size.
There are 7 total parts.
2 parts are shaded.
The denominator is 7, and the numerator is 2: $\frac{2}{7}$.

So, the correct answer is Ⓒ.

Why are the other answer choices not correct?

Ⓐ $\frac{7}{2}$	2 should be the numerator, and 7 should be the denominator.
Ⓑ $\frac{2}{5}$	The denominator should be the total number of parts, not the number of parts that are not painted.
Ⓓ $\frac{5}{7}$	The numerator should be the number of parts that are painted, not the number of parts that are not painted.

Your Turn **Solve each problem. Use the hints to avoid mistakes.**

- Count the total number of parts and the number of shaded parts carefully.
- Write the total number of equal parts as the bottom number. This is the denominator.
- Write the number of shaded parts or the number of parts a point is from zero as the top number. This is the numerator.

3. What fraction does the point on the number line show?

Ⓐ $\frac{1}{2}$

Ⓑ $\frac{1}{3}$

Ⓒ $\frac{1}{4}$

Ⓓ $\frac{2}{4}$

4. What is the denominator of the fraction shown by the model?

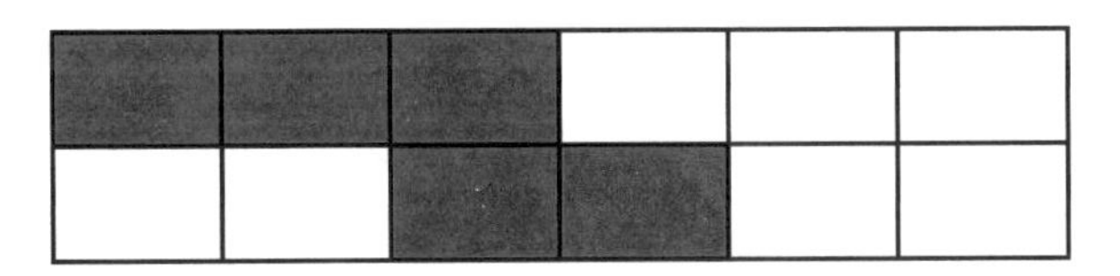

Ⓐ 5

Ⓑ 7

Ⓒ 10

Ⓓ 12

5. Adesh shared a carrot cake with some friends. The shaded parts show the pieces that were left over.

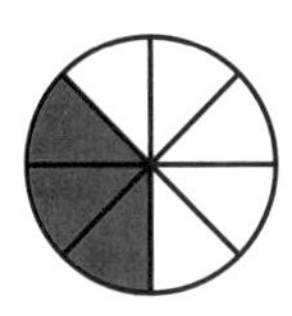

What fraction of the cake was left over?

Ⓐ $\frac{8}{3}$

Ⓑ $\frac{3}{5}$

Ⓒ $\frac{3}{8}$

Ⓓ $\frac{3}{9}$

6. Stacy cut out several shapes to decorate her room.

What fraction of the shapes is shaded?

Ⓐ $\frac{4}{5}$

Ⓑ $\frac{5}{9}$

Ⓒ $\frac{3}{9}$

Ⓓ $\frac{4}{9}$

Study the model. It is a good example of a written answer.

Student Model

Show

Aaron drew a model to show the fraction $\frac{6}{10}$. What might his model look like? Use the grid below to show your answer.

Use pictures, words, or numbers to show your work.

total number of equal parts: 10

number of shaded parts: 6

shaded parts → $\frac{6}{10}$
total parts →

☑ The student shows each step.

Solution:

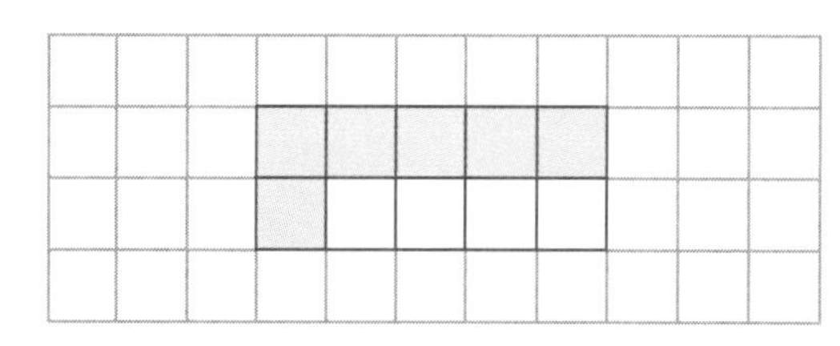

☑ The student correctly answers the question asked.

Explain

Explain how you got your answer.

I know that the denominator of a fraction tells the number of equal parts in the whole. 10 is the denominator of $\frac{6}{10}$, so I divided the whole into 10 equal parts. The numerator tells the number of shaded parts in a whole. 6 is the numerator of $\frac{6}{10}$, so I shaded 6 parts of the whole.

☑ The student gives important details about how to write the fraction.

☑ The student uses the math words *denominator*, *fraction*, *equal parts*, *whole*, and *numerator*.

Your Turn **Solve the problem. Use what you learned from the model.**

7. Tasha drew a number line to show the fraction $\frac{5}{9}$. What might her number line look like? Use the grid below to show your answer.

   Use pictures, words, or numbers to show your work.

CHECKLIST

Did you . . .

- ☐ show each step?
- ☐ answer the question asked?
- ☐ give important details?
- ☐ use math words?

Solution:

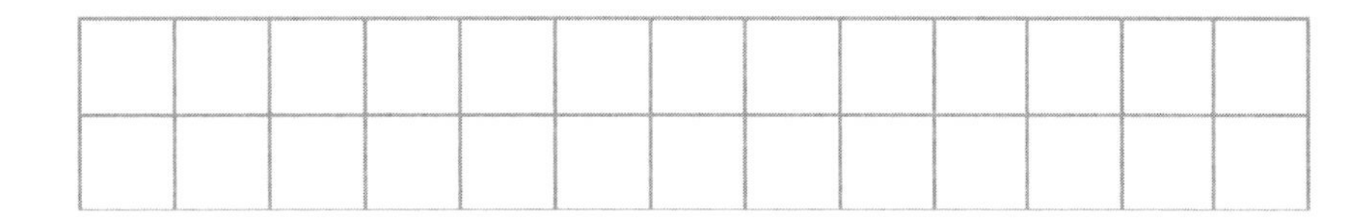

Explain how you got your answer.

____

____

____

____

____

As you solve fraction problems, remember to:

- carefully count the total number of equal parts to find the denominator.
- carefully count the number of shaded parts to find the numerator. Or carefully count the number of parts a point is from zero.
- add the number of shaded parts to the number of parts not shaded to find the total parts, or denominator.

Solve each problem.

8. What fraction does the number line show?

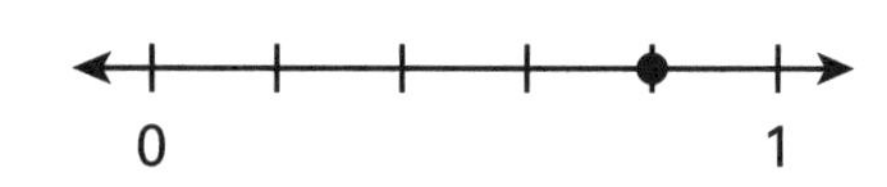

Ⓐ $\frac{1}{5}$

Ⓑ $\frac{4}{5}$

Ⓒ $\frac{4}{6}$

Ⓓ $\frac{5}{6}$

9. Which model shows $\frac{1}{6}$?

Ⓐ 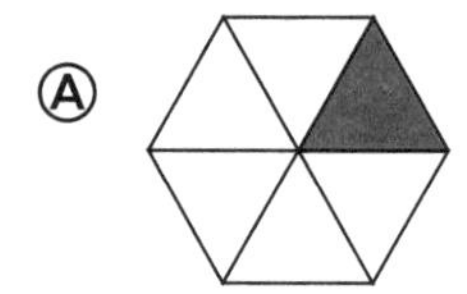

 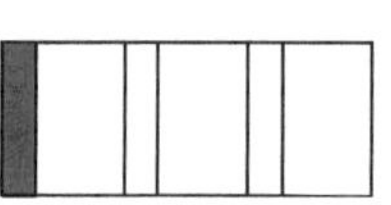

 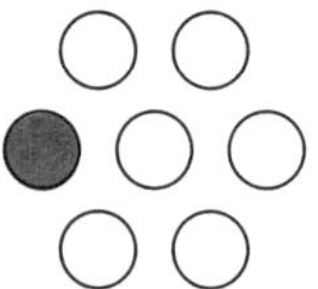

 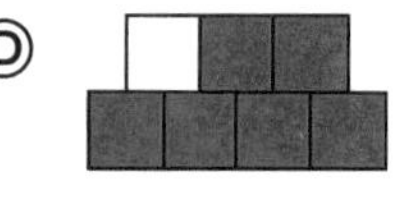

10. Molly mowed the lawn with two friends. They each mowed an equal amount of lawn. The parts that Molly mowed are shaded.

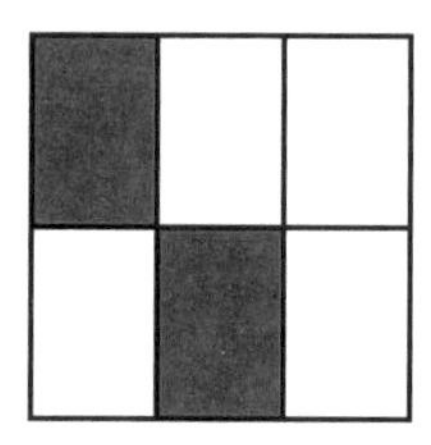

What fraction of the lawn did Molly mow?

Ⓐ $\frac{4}{6}$

Ⓑ $\frac{2}{6}$

Ⓒ $\frac{2}{3}$

Ⓓ $\frac{6}{2}$

11. Mr. Yang has a sheet of white and red star stickers. What fraction of his stickers are red?

Ⓐ $\frac{12}{4}$

Ⓑ $\frac{4}{8}$

Ⓒ $\frac{4}{12}$

Ⓓ $\frac{8}{12}$

12. Which number line shows the fraction $\frac{3}{4}$?

Ⓐ 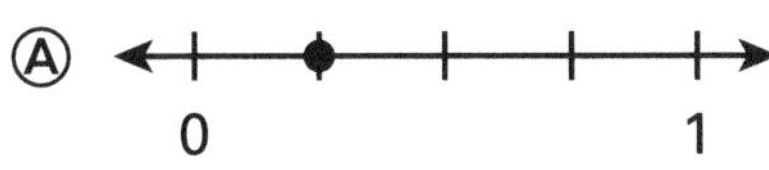

Ⓑ 0 1

Ⓒ 0 1

Ⓓ 0 1

13. What is the numerator of the fraction shown by the point on the number line?

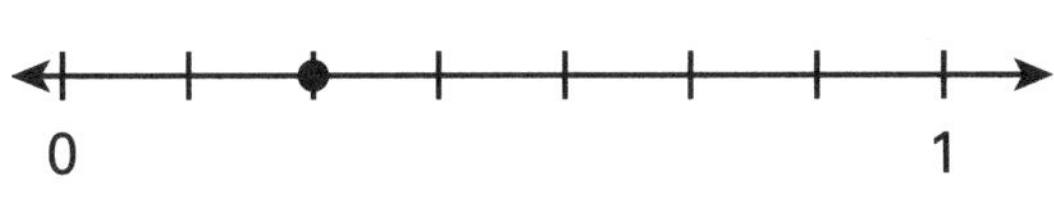

Ⓐ 2

Ⓑ 3

Ⓒ 5

Ⓓ 7

14. Eddison shared a big cookie cake with his friends. The shaded parts show the cake that was left over.

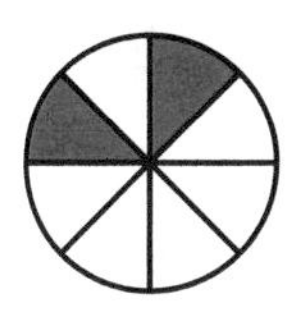

What fraction of the cake was left over? What fraction of the cake did Eddison and his friends eat?

_____ of the cake was left over

_____ of the cake was eaten

15. What number line shows the same fraction as this model?

Use pictures, words, or numbers to show your work.

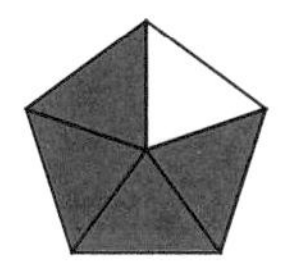

Solution:

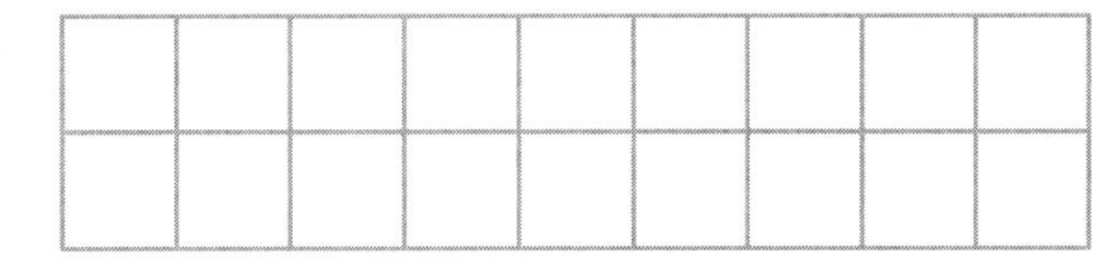

Explain how you found your answer.

____

____

____

____

Lesson 9 MODEL EQUIVALENT FRACTIONS

PART ONE: Learn About Modeling Equivalent Fractions

How can models help you find equivalent fractions?

Explore

A **fraction** names part of a whole that has been divided into equal parts.

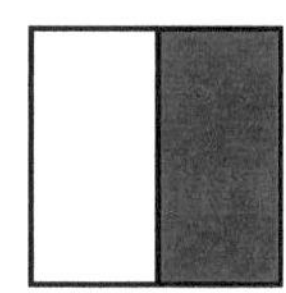

$$\frac{\text{1 part shaded} \rightarrow}{\text{2 parts in all} \rightarrow} \quad \frac{1}{2} \quad \frac{\leftarrow \textbf{numerator}}{\leftarrow \textbf{denominator}}$$

Can different fractions name the same amount of a whole?

Think

Look at the models.

Are they the same size? yes

Is the same amount of each model shaded? yes

What fraction of model A is shaded? $\frac{1}{2}$

What fraction of model B is shaded? $\frac{3}{6}$

A
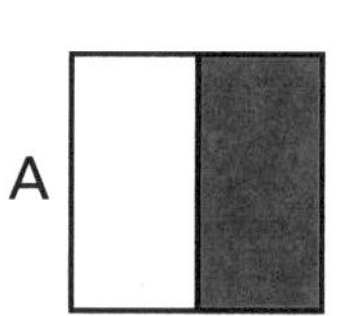

B
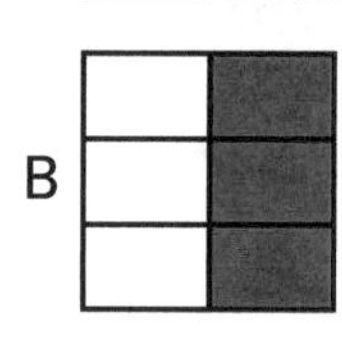

Connect

$\frac{1}{2}$ and $\frac{3}{6}$ name the same amount of a whole.

$\frac{1}{2}$ and $\frac{3}{6}$ are **equivalent fractions**.

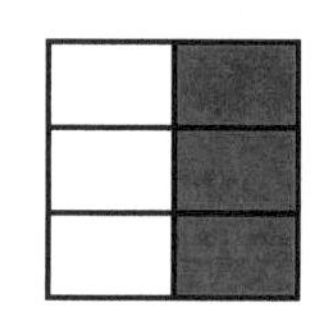

$$\frac{1}{2} = \frac{3}{6}$$

Let's Talk

Explain how the fraction bars show equivalent fractions.

1 whole					
$\frac{1}{2}$			$\frac{1}{2}$		
$\frac{1}{6}$	$\frac{1}{6}$	$\frac{1}{6}$	$\frac{1}{6}$	$\frac{1}{6}$	$\frac{1}{6}$

Fill in the blanks. Solve the problem.

Use the models to find the missing number.

$\frac{2}{6} = \frac{\square}{12}$

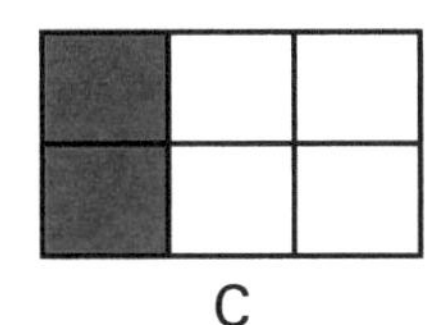

C

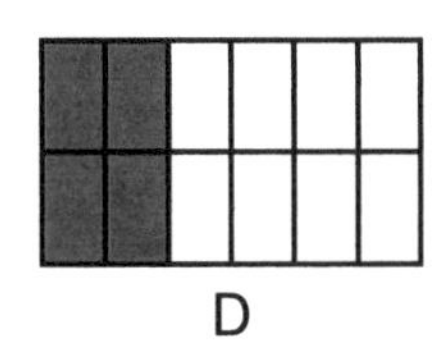

D

- Are the models the same size? _______
- How many total parts does model C have? _______

  How many parts are shaded? _______

  What fraction does C show? _______
- How many total parts does model D have? _______

  How many parts are shaded? _______

  What fraction does D show? _______
- The same amount of each model is shaded.

  So, _______ and _______ are equivalent fractions.

Solution: $\frac{2}{6} = \frac{\square}{12}$

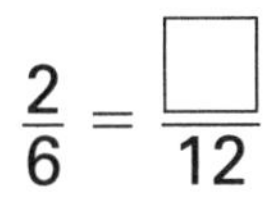

Your Turn **Now, use what you know to solve this problem.**

1. What is the missing number?

$\frac{1}{4} = \frac{\square}{8}$

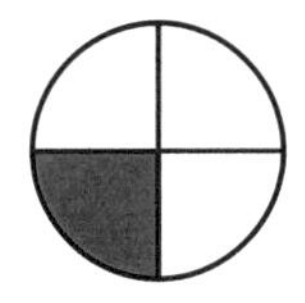

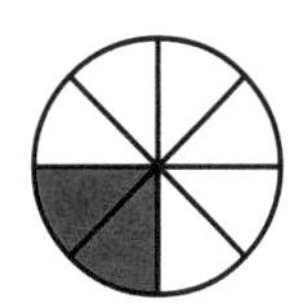

Ⓐ 1
Ⓑ 2
Ⓒ 3
Ⓓ 4

How can number lines help you find equivalent fractions?

Explore

You can use models to show equivalent fractions.

What is another way to show equivalent fractions?

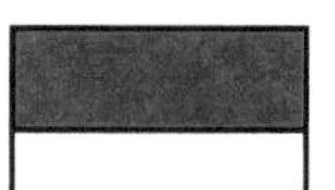

$\frac{1}{2} = \frac{5}{10}$

Think

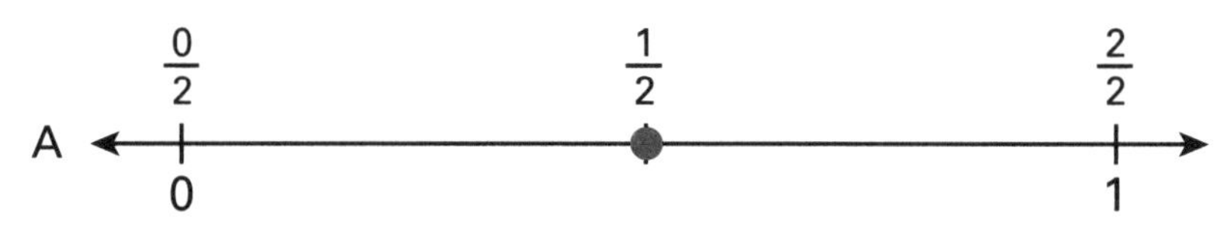

B: $\frac{0}{4}$, $\frac{1}{4}$, $\frac{2}{4}$, $\frac{3}{4}$, $\frac{4}{4}$; 0, 1

How many parts are there between 0 and 1 on number line A? 2

What fraction does the point on number line A show? $\frac{1}{2}$

How many parts are there between 0 and 1 on number line B? 4

What fraction does the point on number line B show? $\frac{2}{4}$

Connect

Number lines are another way to show equivalent fractions.

The points on number lines A and B show the fractions $\frac{1}{2}$ and $\frac{2}{4}$.

These fractions are both the same distance from 0.

So, $\frac{1}{2} = \frac{2}{4}$.

Let's Talk

How can you tell from the number lines above that $\frac{4}{4} = \frac{2}{2}$?

Fill in the blanks. Solve the problem.

A point on number line C shows a fraction. What is the fraction? What is the equivalent fraction on number line D?

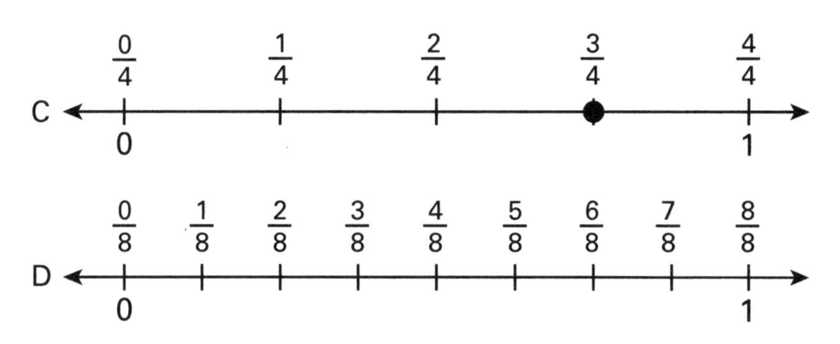

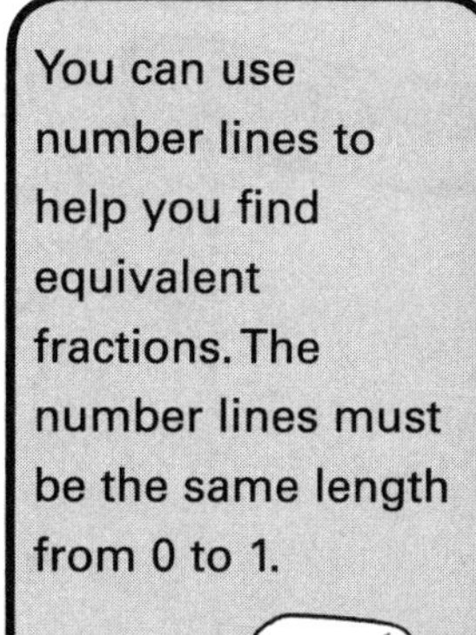

- What fraction does the point on C show? _______
- Draw a point on D that is the same distance from 0 as the point on C.

  What fraction does the point on D show? _______
- The fractions are both the same distance from 0.

  So, _______ and _______ are equivalent fractions.

Solution: $\frac{\square}{\square} = \frac{\square}{\square}$

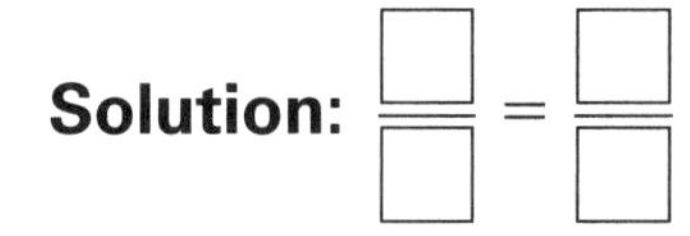

Now, use what you know to solve this problem.

2. Use the number lines to find the missing number.

$$\frac{2}{4} = \frac{\square}{6}$$

$\frac{0}{4}$ $\frac{1}{4}$ $\frac{2}{4}$ $\frac{3}{4}$ $\frac{4}{4}$

0 1

$\frac{0}{6}$ $\frac{1}{6}$ $\frac{2}{6}$ $\frac{3}{6}$ $\frac{4}{6}$ $\frac{5}{6}$ $\frac{6}{6}$

0 1

PART THREE: Choose the Right Answer

Solve the problem. Then read why each answer choice is correct or not correct.

Solve

Ida's family ate $\frac{4}{6}$ of a cherry pie. 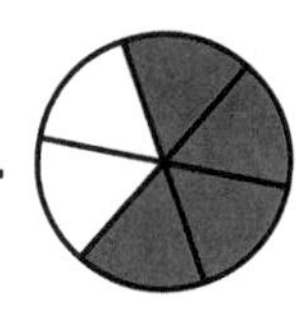

Kasem's family ate the same amount of an apple pie. Which shows the amount of pie Kasem's family ate?

Ⓐ $\frac{2}{3}$ 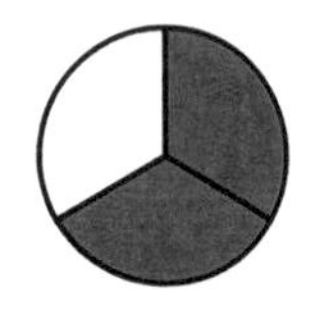

Ⓑ $\frac{2}{4}$ 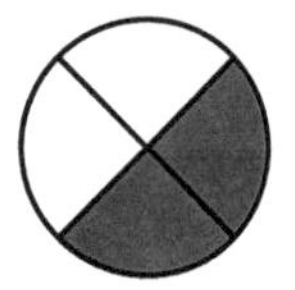

Ⓒ $\frac{2}{6}$ 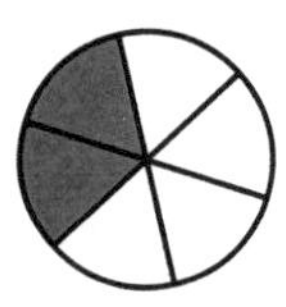

Ⓓ $\frac{7}{8}$ 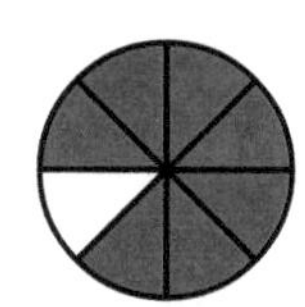

Check

Check to see if you chose the correct answer.

The models are the same size.

The model for $\frac{2}{3}$ shows the same amount shaded as the model for $\frac{4}{6}$.

So, the correct answer is Ⓐ.

Why are the other answer choices not correct?

Ⓑ $\frac{2}{4}$ 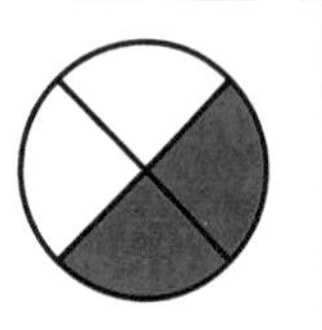	This model shows a smaller amount shaded than $\frac{4}{6}$.
Ⓒ $\frac{2}{6}$ 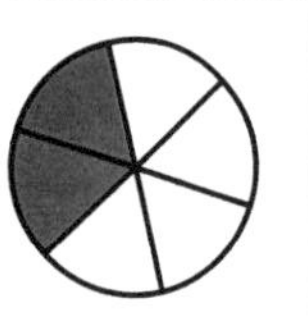	This is the fraction of pie that Ida's family didn't eat.
Ⓓ $\frac{7}{8}$ 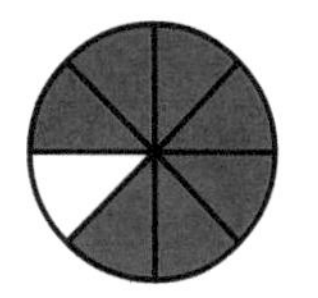	This model shows a larger amount shaded than $\frac{4}{6}$.

Your Turn **Solve each problem. Use the hints to avoid mistakes.**

- Carefully compare models to find equivalent fractions. Make sure the same amount is shaded in each one.
- Carefully compare number lines to find equivalent fractions. Make sure the fractions are the same distance from 0.

Use the number lines for problems 3 and 4.

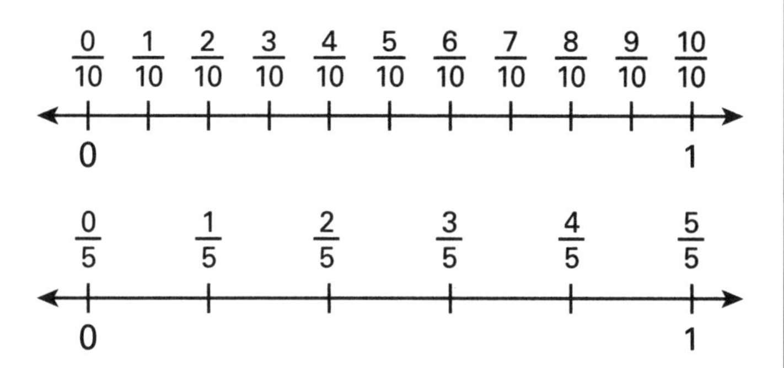

3. Which fraction is equivalent to $\frac{6}{10}$?

Ⓐ $\frac{1}{5}$ Ⓒ $\frac{3}{5}$

Ⓑ $\frac{2}{5}$ Ⓓ $\frac{4}{5}$

4. Which fraction is equivalent to $\frac{2}{5}$?

Ⓐ $\frac{2}{10}$ Ⓒ $\frac{5}{10}$

Ⓑ $\frac{4}{10}$ Ⓓ $\frac{6}{10}$

5. What is the missing number?

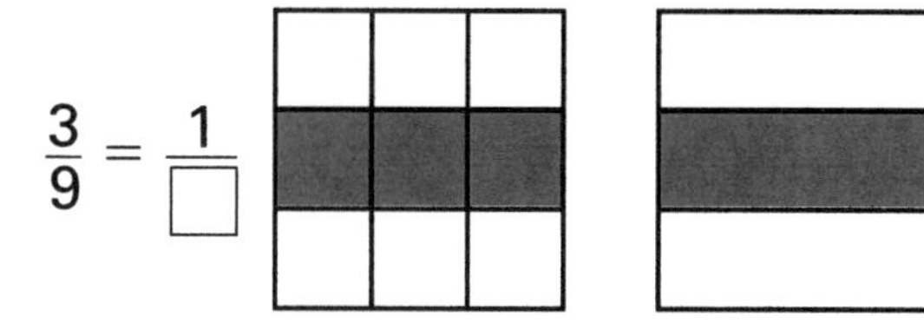

Ⓐ 2 Ⓒ 6

Ⓑ 3 Ⓓ 9

6. Kim wants to fill $\frac{1}{2}$ of a serving plate with carrot sticks. If the plate is divided into six parts, how many parts should Kim fill with carrots?

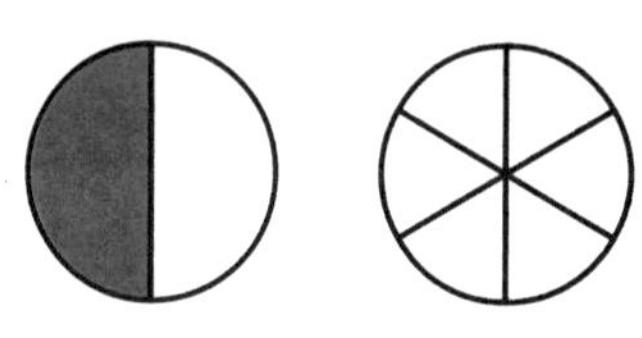

Ⓐ 1 Ⓒ 3

Ⓑ 2 Ⓓ 6

Study the model. It is a good example of a written answer.

Student Model

Show

Mary, Joel, Sam, and Eliza each baked a pan of brownies. The shaded part of each pan shows the amount of brownies each person ate.

Mary's Pan | Joel's Pan | Sam's Pan | Eliza's Pan

Find the fraction of brownies that was eaten from each pan. Then write the fractions that are equivalent.

Use pictures, words, or numbers to show your work.

Mary: $\frac{1}{4}$ eaten   Sam: $\frac{2}{8}$ eaten

Joel: $\frac{2}{6}$ eaten   Eliza: $\frac{4}{10}$ eaten

Mary and Sam have the same amount shaded, so $\frac{1}{4} = \frac{2}{8}$.

Solution: $\frac{1}{4}$ and $\frac{2}{8}$ are equivalent fractions.

Explain

Explain how you got your answer.

First, I named the fraction for each pan. I put the total number of parts in the denominator and the number of shaded parts in the numerator. Then I saw that Mary and Sam's pans have the same amount shaded. So, I knew that $\frac{1}{4}$ is equivalent to $\frac{2}{8}$.

☑ The student shows each step.

☑ The student correctly answers the question asked.

☑ The student gives important details about how to find equivalent fractions.

☑ The student uses math words like *fraction, denominator, numerator,* and *equivalent.*

Your Turn **Solve the problem. Use what you learned from the model.**

CHECKLIST

Did you . . .

- ☐ show each step?
- ☐ answer the question asked?
- ☐ give important details?
- ☐ use math words?

7. Jaycee, Tonell, and Darryl each have a box with spaces for storing beads. The boxes are the same size, but each one has a different number of spaces. Jaycee filled 1 part of her box. Tonell filled 2 parts of his box. Darryl filled 3 parts of his box.

Jaycee's Box

Tonell's Box

Darryl's Box

Find the fraction of each box that was filled.
Then tell who filled the same amount of their boxes.

Use pictures, words, or numbers to show your work.

Solution: __________ and __________ filled the same amount of their containers.

Explain how you got your answer.

____

____

____

____

____

As you solve equivalent fractions problems, you may want to
- shade models or draw points on number lines to see if fractions are equivalent.
- move your finger straight up or down from a fraction on one number line to find an equivalent fraction on another number line.

Solve each problem.

8. Which fraction is equivalent to $\frac{1}{4}$?

1 whole							
$\frac{1}{4}$		$\frac{1}{4}$		$\frac{1}{4}$		$\frac{1}{4}$	
$\frac{1}{8}$	$\frac{1}{8}$	$\frac{1}{8}$	$\frac{1}{8}$	$\frac{1}{8}$	$\frac{1}{8}$	$\frac{1}{8}$	$\frac{1}{8}$

Ⓐ $\frac{2}{16}$
Ⓑ $\frac{2}{8}$
Ⓒ $\frac{1}{8}$
Ⓓ $\frac{1}{2}$

9. Howard and Jill are covering pillows with fabric. They both cover the same amount of their pillows. Howard covers $\frac{4}{8}$ of his pillow. Which shows how much of her pillow Jill covers?

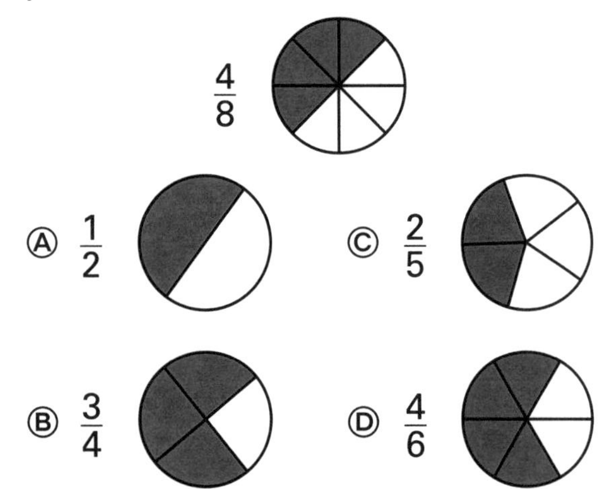

Use the number lines below for problems 10 and 11.

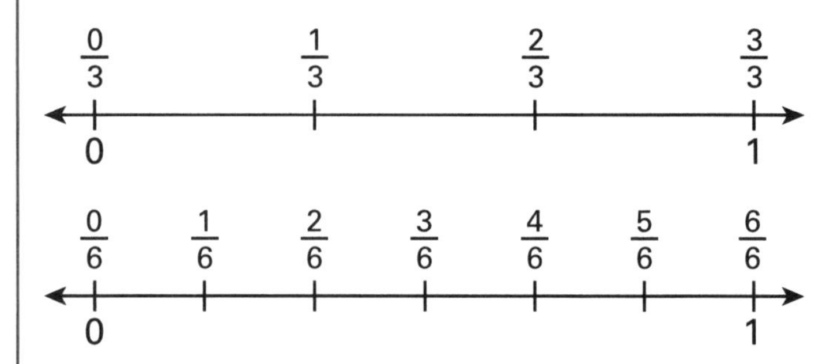

10. Which fraction is equivalent to $\frac{2}{6}$?

Ⓐ $\frac{0}{3}$
Ⓑ $\frac{1}{3}$
Ⓒ $\frac{2}{3}$
Ⓓ $\frac{3}{3}$

11. Which two fractions are **not** equivalent?

Ⓐ $\frac{0}{3}$ and $\frac{0}{6}$
Ⓑ $\frac{1}{3}$ and $\frac{1}{6}$
Ⓒ $\frac{2}{3}$ and $\frac{4}{6}$
Ⓓ $\frac{3}{3}$ and $\frac{6}{6}$

12. What is the missing number?

$\frac{4}{6} = \frac{\square}{12}$

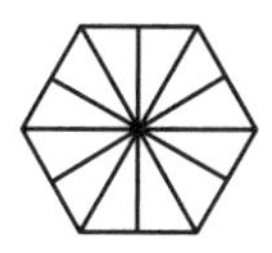

Ⓐ 0

Ⓑ 4

Ⓒ 8

Ⓓ 9

13. How many parts should be shaded in model B so the models show equivalent fractions?

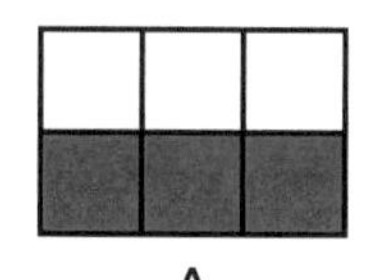

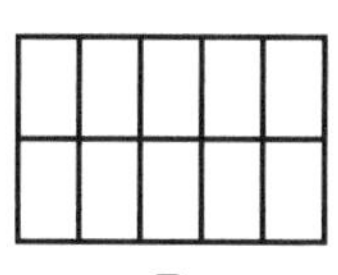

Ⓐ 0

Ⓑ 3

Ⓒ 5

Ⓓ 6

14. Katarina wants to put $\frac{1}{2}$ of the ice cubes in her tray into a pitcher. Her tray is divided into 12 parts. How many parts should she empty?

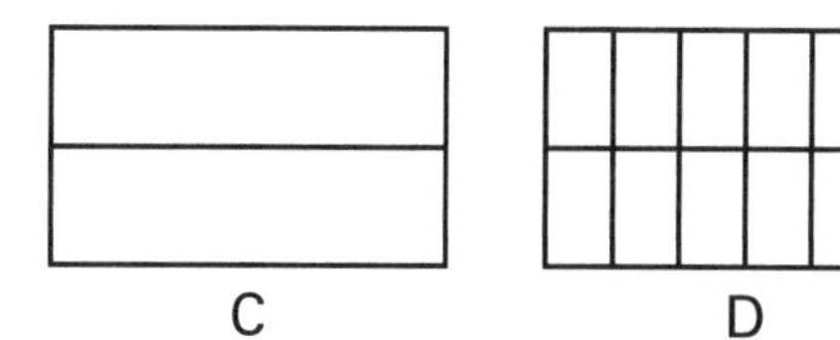

Shade the models to show the equivalent fractions.

Katarina should empty _______ parts of the tray.

15. Ken ran $\frac{3}{4}$ mile, Mariah ran $\frac{2}{6}$ mile, and Jermaine ran $\frac{6}{8}$ mile. Who ran the same distance?

Use pictures, words, or numbers to show your work.

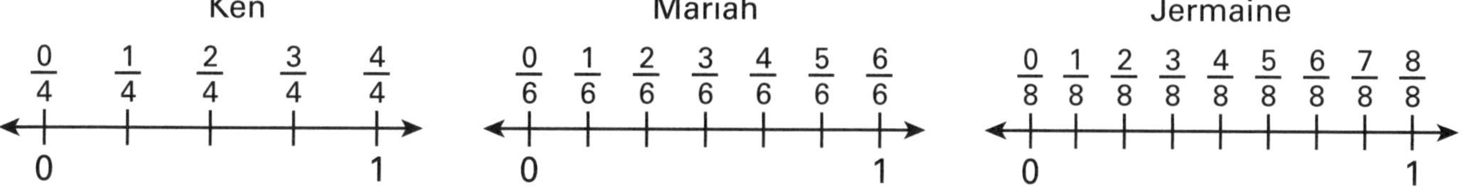

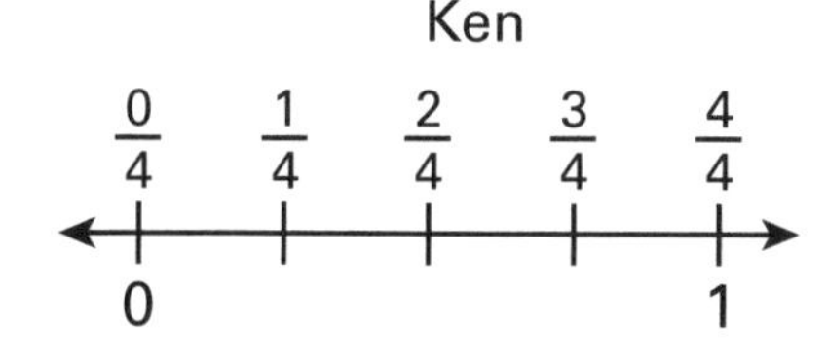

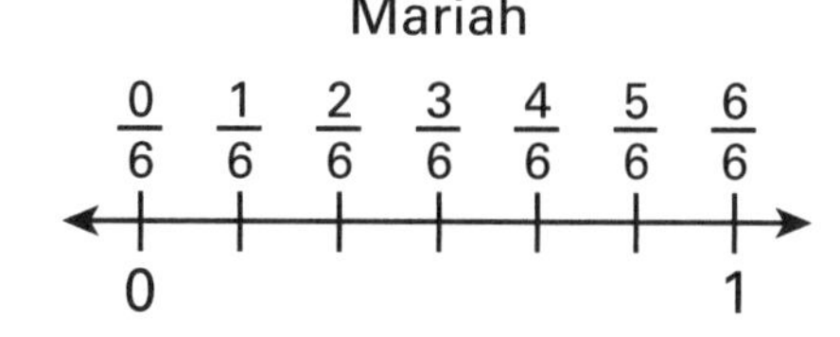

Solution: __________ and __________ ran the same distance.

Explain how you got your answer.

____

____

____

____

Lesson 10 BENCHMARK FRACTIONS

PART ONE: Learn About Comparing Fractions to $\frac{1}{2}$

How can you compare fractions to $\frac{1}{2}$?

Explore

Models can show **fractions** that are **equivalent** to $\frac{1}{2}$.

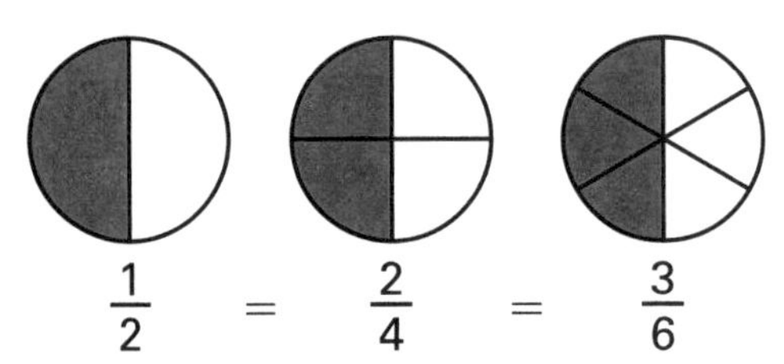

$\frac{1}{2} = \frac{2}{4} = \frac{3}{6}$

How can you tell if fractions are more or less than $\frac{1}{2}$?

Think

Look at the models.

Are they the same size and shape? yes

What fraction of model A is shaded? $\frac{2}{5}$

What fraction of model B is shaded? $\frac{1}{2}$

Which model has less shading? A

A 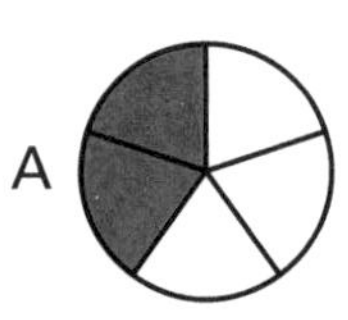

B 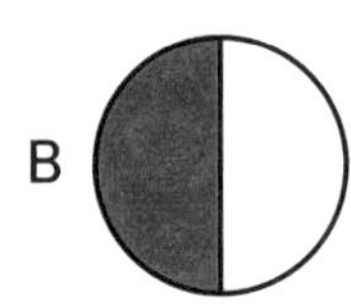

Connect

You can use models to **compare** fractions to $\frac{1}{2}$.

When you compare numbers, you decide which is **greater than** (>) or **less than** (<) the other.

Model A has less shading than model B.

So, $\frac{2}{5}$ is less than $\frac{1}{2}$.

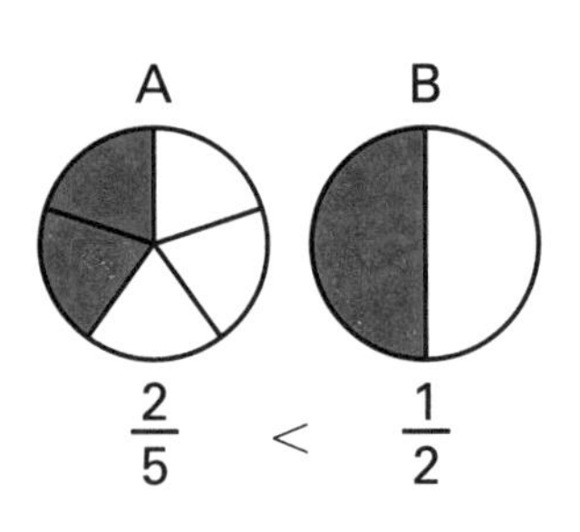

$\frac{2}{5} < \frac{1}{2}$

Let's Talk

Use model A to find other fractions less than $\frac{1}{2}$. Then find fractions greater than $\frac{1}{2}$. Explain how you got each answer.

Fill in the blanks. Solve the problem.

Michelle and her friends ate $\frac{5}{8}$ of a pizza.
Did they eat more than or less than $\frac{1}{2}$ of a pizza?

- You can use a number line to solve the problem.

  How many total parts did the pizza have? ____

  The number line is divided into that many parts.

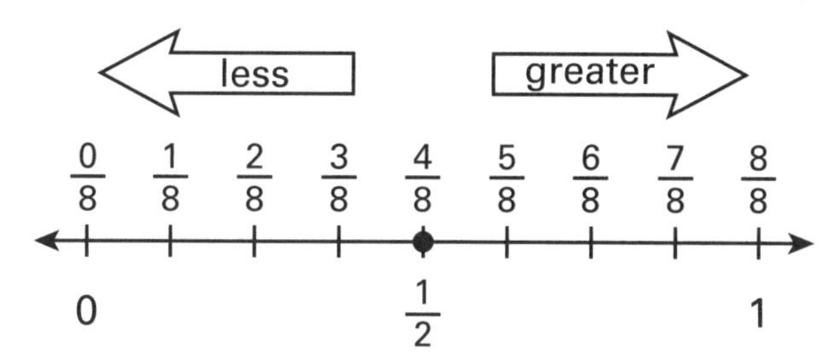

On a number line, fractions to the left of $\frac{1}{2}$ are less than $\frac{1}{2}$. Fractions to the right of $\frac{1}{2}$ are greater than $\frac{1}{2}$.

- Draw a point to show the fraction of the pizza that Michelle and her friends ate.

  How many parts of the pizza did they eat? ______

  How many parts from 0 should you draw the point? ______

- Is $\frac{5}{8}$ to the left or right of $\frac{1}{2}$? ___________
- $\frac{5}{8}$ is to the ___________ of $\frac{1}{2}$, so $\frac{5}{8}$ is ___________ $\frac{1}{2}$.

  Or $\frac{5}{8}$ ______ $\frac{1}{2}$.

Solution: Michelle and her friends ate ___________ $\frac{1}{2}$ a pizza.

Now, use what you know to solve this problem.

1. Which fraction is less than $\frac{1}{2}$?

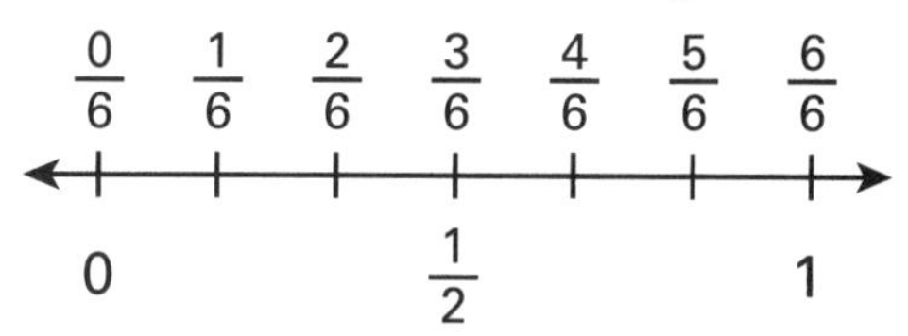

Ⓐ $\frac{4}{6}$ Ⓑ $\frac{1}{6}$ Ⓒ $\frac{5}{6}$ Ⓓ $\frac{3}{6}$

How can you tell if a fraction is closer to 0 or 1?

Explore

A fraction names 1 or more **equal parts** of a whole.

The **numerator** tells the number of shaded parts.

The **denominator** tells the total number of parts.

$\frac{3}{9}$ ← shaded / 3 shaded + 6 not shaded

How can comparing shaded parts to not shaded parts help you decide if a fraction is closer to 0 or 1?

Think

How many parts is the whole divided into? 8

How many parts are shaded? 3

What fraction is shaded? $\frac{3}{8}$

How many parts of the whole are not shaded? 5

Connect

When the whole has more parts shaded than not shaded, the fraction is closer to 1.

When the whole has fewer parts shaded than not shaded, the fraction is closer to 0.

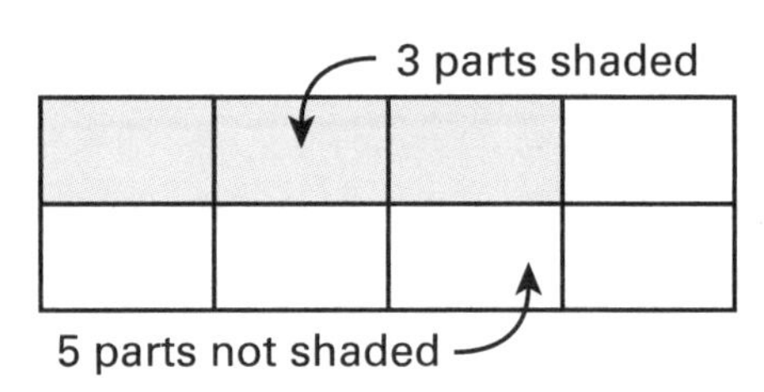

In the model for $\frac{3}{8}$, 3 parts are shaded and 5 parts are not shaded.

$3 < 5$, so fewer parts are shaded.

$\frac{3}{8}$ is closer to 0 than 1.

Let's Talk

If a fraction is less than $\frac{1}{2}$, is it closer to 0 or 1? How do you know?

Fill in the blanks. Solve the problem.

Mary finished $\frac{7}{8}$ of her painting. Is $\frac{7}{8}$ closer to 0 or 1?

- You can use a number line to solve the problem.

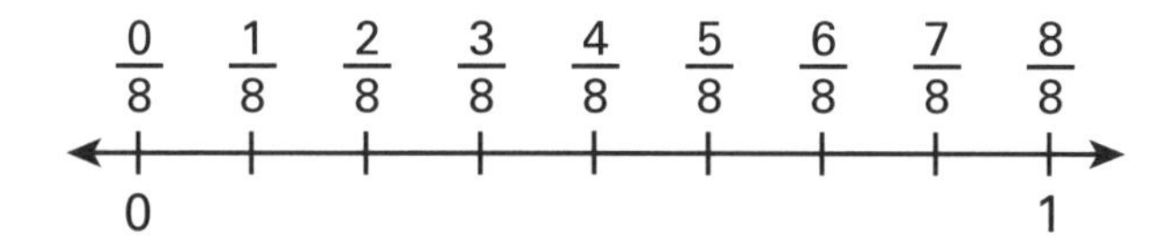

Draw a point to show 0 on the number line.

Draw a point to show 1 on the number line.

Draw a point to show $\frac{7}{8}$ on the number line.

- How many parts away from 0 is $\frac{7}{8}$? ______
- How many parts away from 1 is $\frac{7}{8}$? ______
- 1 _____ 7, so $\frac{7}{8}$ is ______ parts away from 1 than 0.

Solution: $\frac{7}{8}$ is closer to ______ than ______.

When a fraction is fewer parts away from 0 than 1, the fraction is closer to 0.

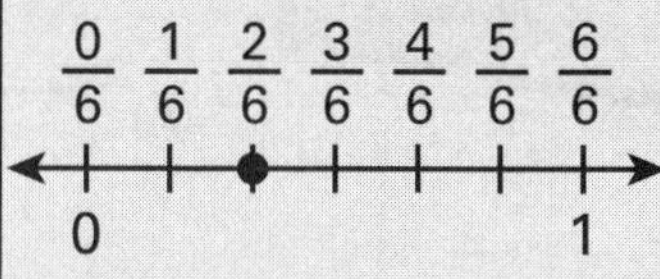

2 parts away from 0

4 parts away from 1

$2 < 4$, so $\frac{2}{6}$ is closer to 0.

When a fraction is fewer parts away from 1 than 0, the fraction is closer to 1.

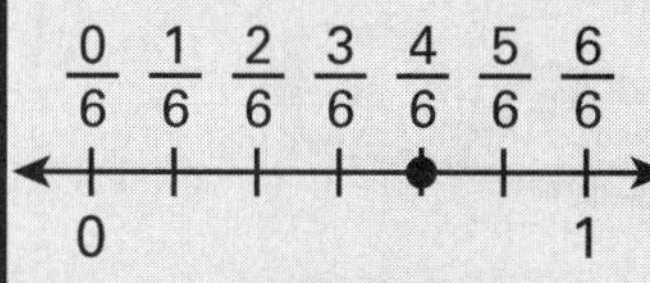

2 parts away from 1

4 parts away from 0

$2 < 4$, so $\frac{4}{6}$ is closer to 1.

Now, use what you know to solve this problem.

2. In Ms. Jones's class, $\frac{3}{8}$ of the students have a pet. Is $\frac{3}{8}$ closer to 0 or 1? You can use the number line above to help you.

$\frac{3}{8}$ is closer to ______.

PART THREE: Choose the Right Answer

Solve the problem. Then read why each answer choice is correct or not correct.

Solve

Which fraction is greater than $\frac{1}{2}$?

 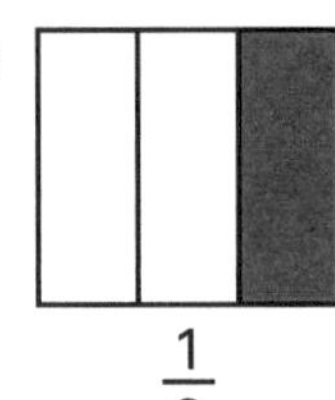 $\frac{1}{3}$

Ⓑ 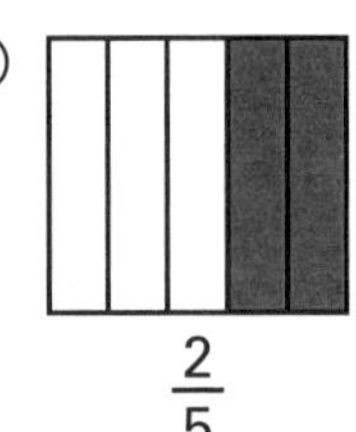 $\frac{2}{5}$

Ⓒ 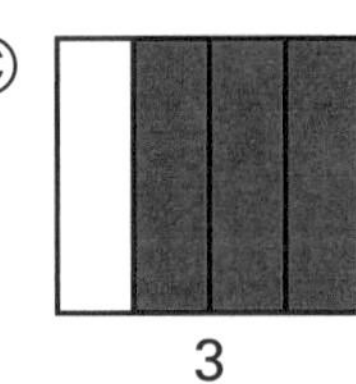 $\frac{3}{4}$

Ⓓ 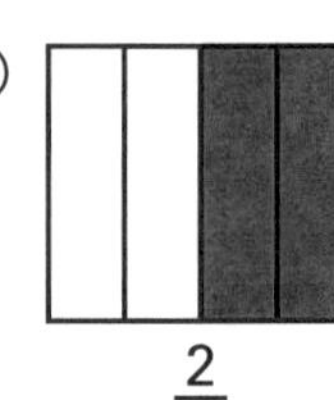 $\frac{2}{4}$

Check

Check to see that you chose the correct answer.

A model that has more parts shaded than not shaded shows a fraction greater than $\frac{1}{2}$.

The model for $\frac{3}{4}$ shows 3 parts shaded and 1 part not shaded.

This means $\frac{3}{4}$ is greater than $\frac{1}{2}$.

So, the correct answer is Ⓒ.

Why are the other answer choices not correct?

Ⓐ $\frac{1}{3}$	The model shows 1 part shaded and 2 parts not shaded. There are more parts not shaded than shaded.
Ⓑ $\frac{2}{5}$	The model shows 2 parts shaded and 3 parts not shaded. There are fewer parts shaded than not shaded.
Ⓓ $\frac{2}{4}$	The model shows 2 parts shaded and 2 parts not shaded. The number of parts shaded is equal to the number of parts not shaded.

Your Turn **Solve each problem. Use the hints to avoid mistakes.**

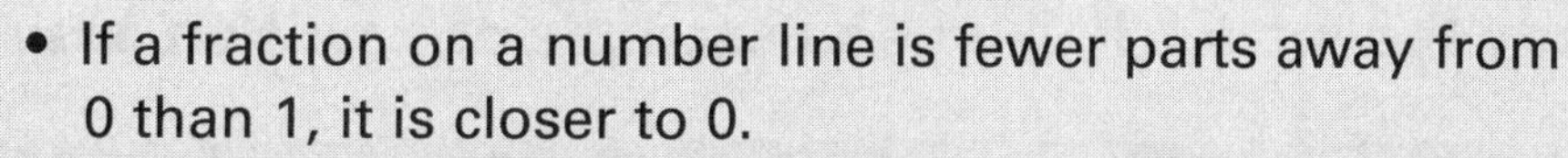

- If a fraction on a number line is fewer parts away from 0 than 1, it is closer to 0.
- If a fraction on a number line is fewer parts away from 1 than 0, it is closer to 1.

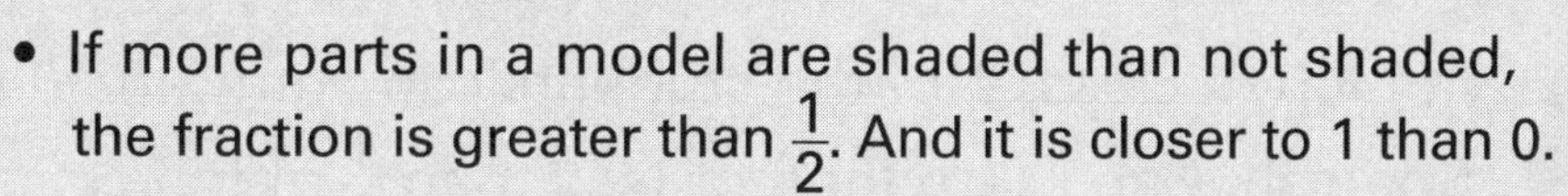

- If more parts in a model are shaded than not shaded, the fraction is greater than $\frac{1}{2}$. And it is closer to 1 than 0.
- If more parts of a model are not shaded than shaded, the fraction is less than $\frac{1}{2}$. And it is closer to 0 than 1.

3. Which fraction is less than $\frac{1}{2}$?

Ⓐ 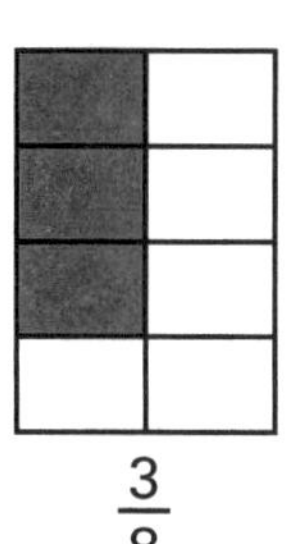

$\frac{3}{8}$

Ⓒ 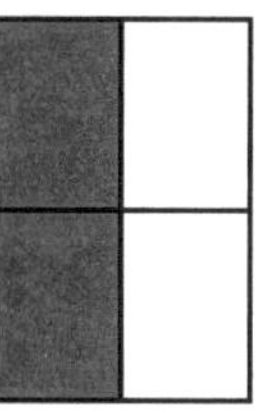

$\frac{2}{4}$

Ⓑ 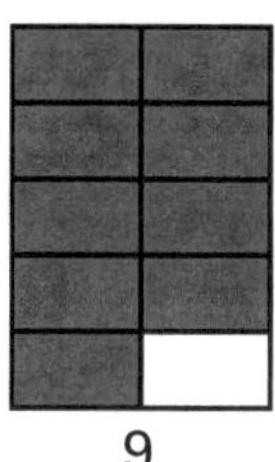

$\frac{9}{10}$

Ⓓ 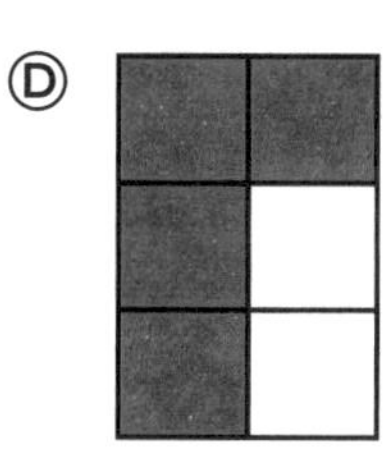

$\frac{4}{6}$

4. Which fraction is closest to 0?

Ⓐ 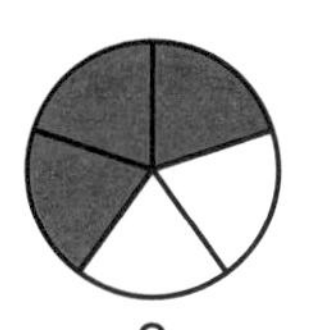

$\frac{3}{5}$

Ⓒ 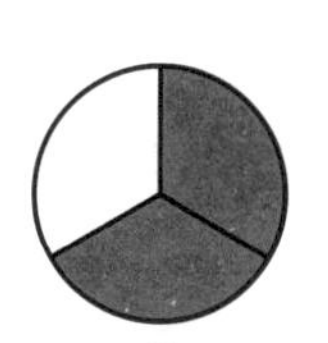

$\frac{2}{3}$

Ⓑ 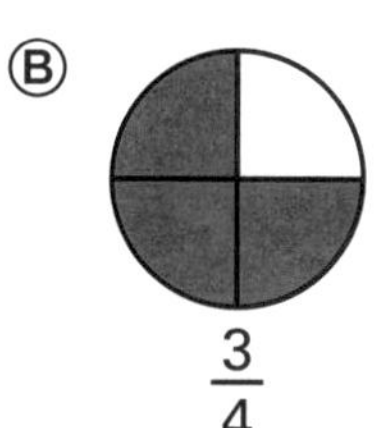

$\frac{3}{4}$

Ⓓ 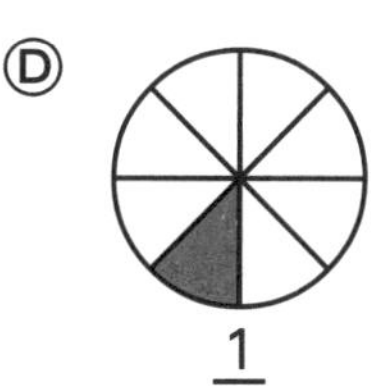

$\frac{1}{8}$

5. Which fraction is closest to 1? You can shade the model to help you.

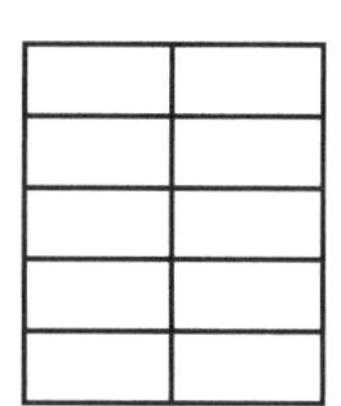

Ⓐ $\frac{2}{10}$

Ⓒ $\frac{7}{10}$

Ⓑ $\frac{4}{10}$

Ⓓ $\frac{5}{10}$

6. Which fraction is greater than $\frac{1}{2}$?

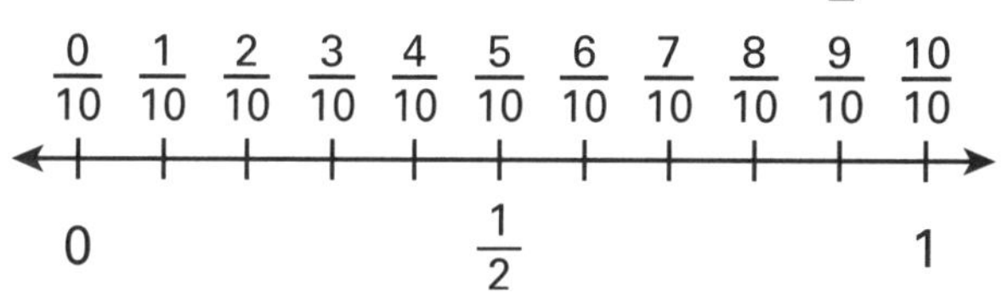

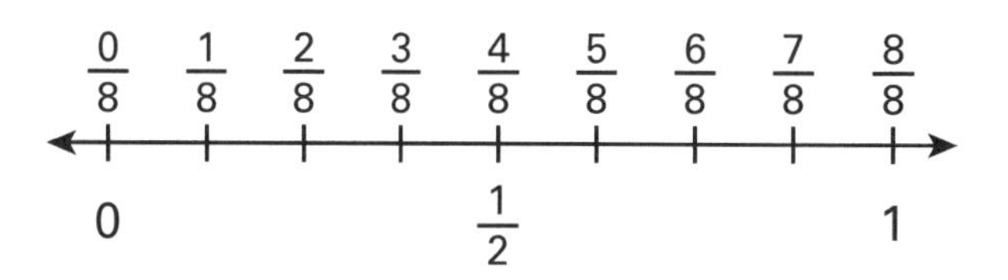

Ⓐ $\frac{5}{10}$

Ⓒ $\frac{3}{10}$

Ⓑ $\frac{5}{8}$

Ⓓ $\frac{3}{8}$

Study the model. It is a good example of a written answer.

Student Model

Show

In Libby's class, $\frac{1}{3}$ of the students can count to 10 in Spanish. Can more than or less than $\frac{1}{2}$ of the class count to 10 in Spanish?

Use pictures, words, or numbers to show your work.

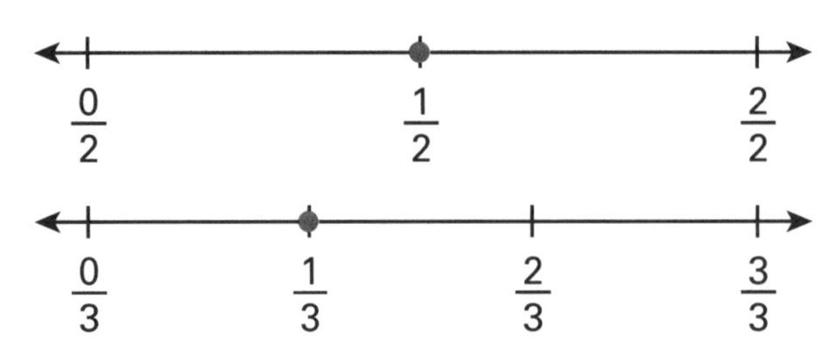

$\frac{1}{3}$ is to the left of $\frac{1}{2}$.

$\frac{1}{3} < \frac{1}{2}$

Solution: Less than $\frac{1}{2}$ of Libby's class can count to 10 in Spanish.

☑ The student shows each step.

☑ The student correctly answers the question asked.

Explain

Explain how you got your answer.

I drew points on the number lines to show $\frac{1}{3}$ and $\frac{1}{2}$. Then I used the number lines to compare the fractions. I saw that $\frac{1}{3}$ is to the left of $\frac{1}{2}$, so I know that $\frac{1}{3}$ is less than $\frac{1}{2}$. Less than $\frac{1}{2}$ of Libby's class can count to 10 in Spanish.

☑ The student gives important details about how to compare the fraction to $\frac{1}{2}$.

☑ The student uses math words like *number line*, *compare*, *fractions*, and *less than*.

Your Turn **Solve the problem. Use what you learned from the model.**

7. In a parking lot, $\frac{6}{10}$ of the cars have five or more seats. Do more than or less than $\frac{1}{2}$ of the cars have five or more seats?

Use pictures, words, or numbers to show your work.

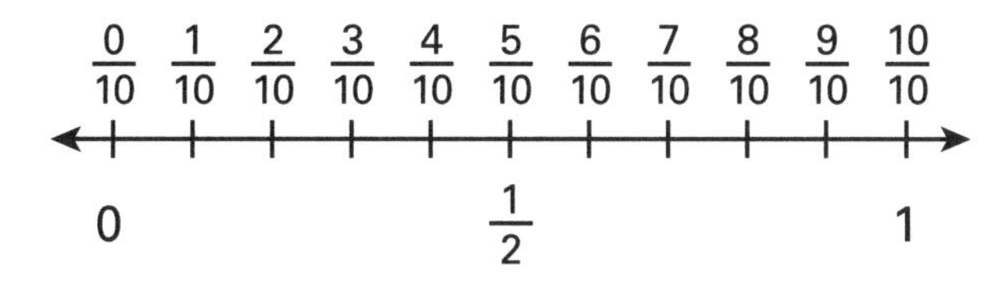

CHECKLIST

Did you . . .

- ☐ show each step?
- ☐ answer the question asked?
- ☐ give important details?
- ☐ use math words?

Solution: ________________ $\frac{1}{2}$ of the cars have five or more seats.

Explain how you got your answer.

____

____

____

____

____

As you solve problems comparing fractions,
- carefully count the shaded and not shaded parts of a model to compare them.
- determine if a fraction is fewer parts away from 0 on a number line or fewer parts away from 1.

Solve each problem.

8. Which fraction is closest to 1?

Ⓐ 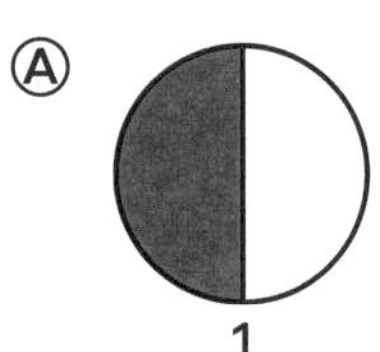
$\frac{1}{2}$

Ⓒ 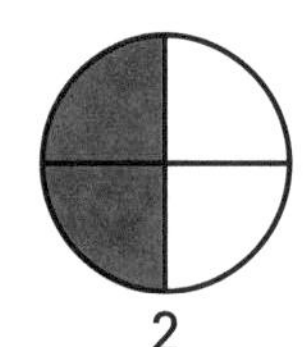
$\frac{2}{4}$

Ⓑ 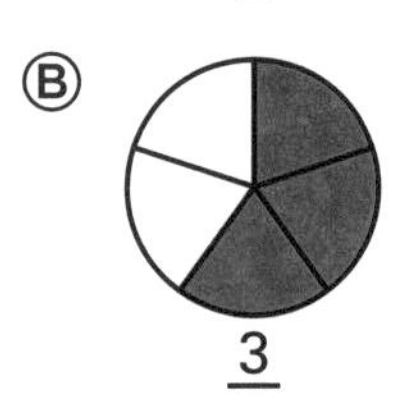
$\frac{3}{5}$

Ⓓ 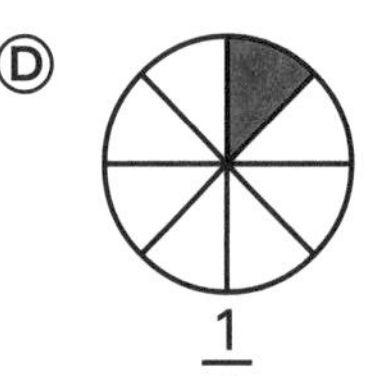
$\frac{1}{8}$

9. Which model shows a fraction greater than $\frac{1}{2}$?

Ⓐ 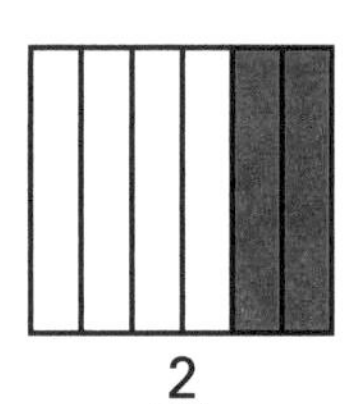
$\frac{2}{6}$

Ⓒ 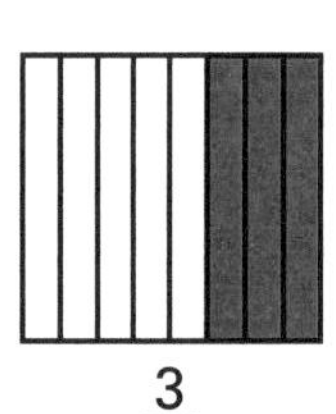
$\frac{3}{8}$

Ⓑ 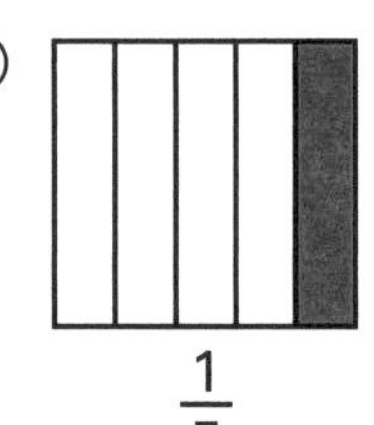
$\frac{1}{5}$

Ⓓ 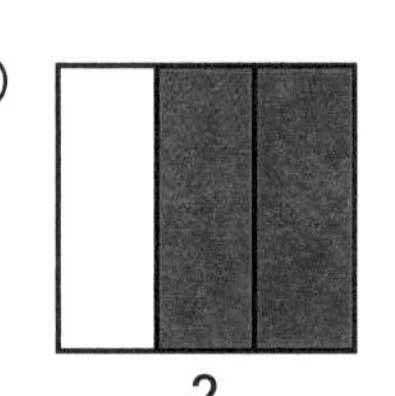
$\frac{2}{3}$

10. Kiara ate $\frac{2}{5}$ of a pie. Hireo ate $\frac{2}{3}$ of a pie. Which is true?

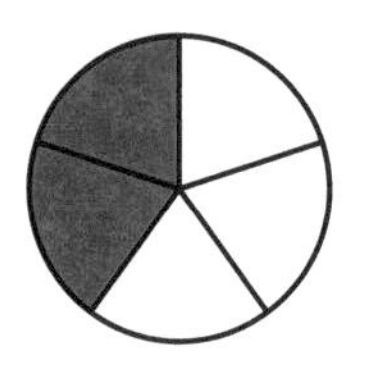
$\frac{2}{5}$

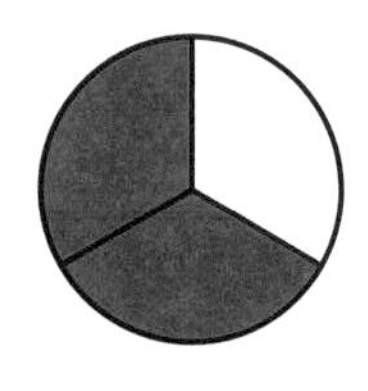
$\frac{2}{3}$

Ⓐ Kiara was closer to eating a whole pie than Hireo.

Ⓑ Hireo and Kiara ate the same amount of pie.

Ⓒ Hireo was closer to eating a whole pie than Kiara.

Ⓓ Kiara ate more pie than Hireo.

11. Which is true?

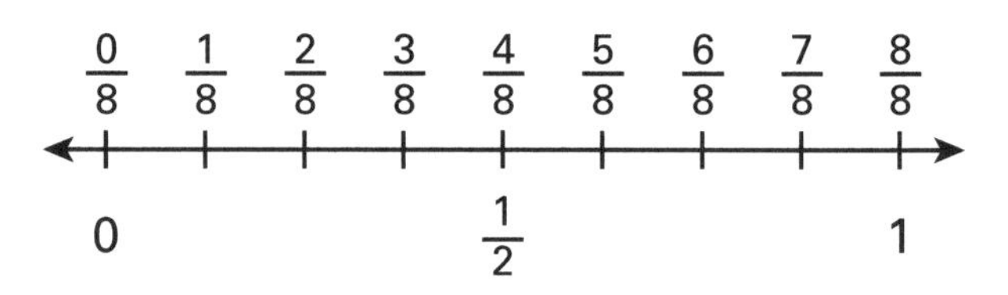

Ⓐ $\frac{5}{8} < \frac{1}{2}$

Ⓒ $\frac{2}{8} = \frac{1}{2}$

Ⓑ $\frac{7}{8} > \frac{1}{2}$

Ⓓ $\frac{6}{8} < \frac{1}{2}$

12. Which fraction is greater than $\frac{1}{2}$?

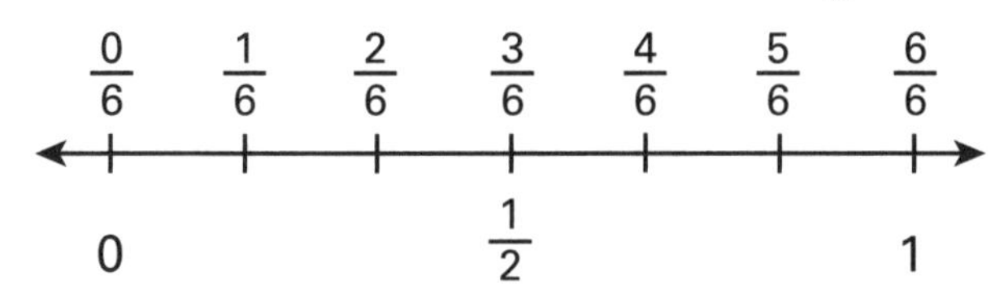

Ⓐ $\frac{1}{6}$

Ⓑ $\frac{4}{6}$

Ⓒ $\frac{3}{6}$

Ⓓ $\frac{2}{6}$

13. Which fraction is closest to 0?

Ⓐ 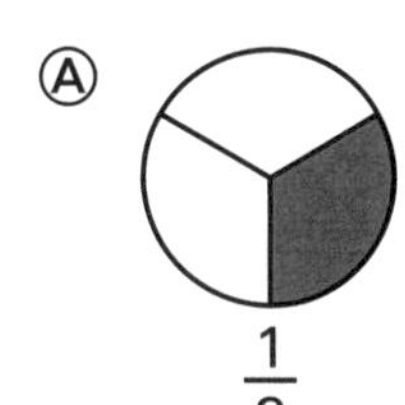

$\frac{1}{3}$

Ⓒ 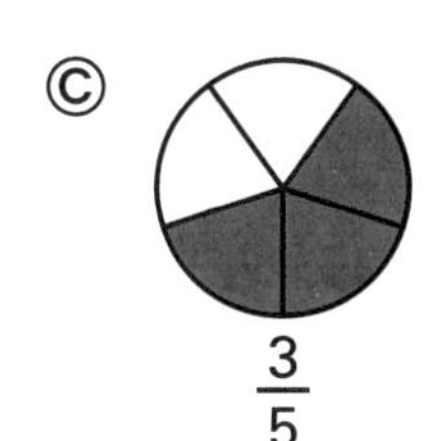

$\frac{3}{5}$

Ⓑ 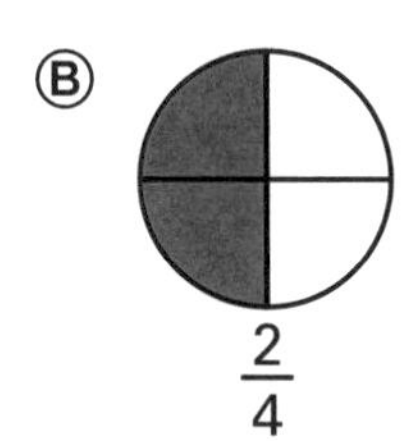

$\frac{2}{4}$

Ⓓ 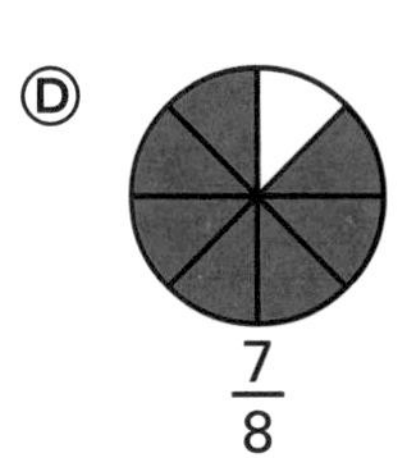

$\frac{7}{8}$

14. Shade the square to show $\frac{1}{4}$.

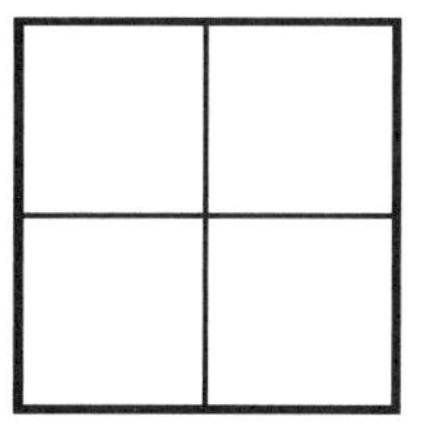

Shade the square to show $\frac{1}{2}$.

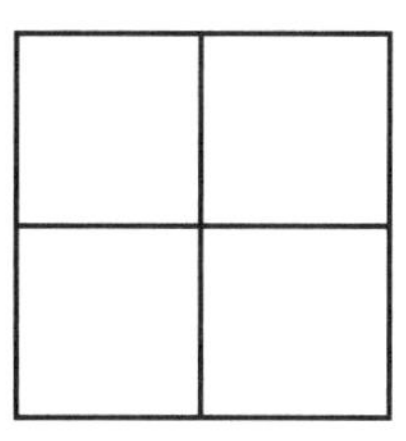

Which fraction is closer to 0? ______

15. At soccer practice, Daria's team spends $\frac{2}{5}$ of the time playing a game. Is more than or less than $\frac{1}{2}$ of the practice time spent playing a game?

Use pictures, words, or numbers to show your work.

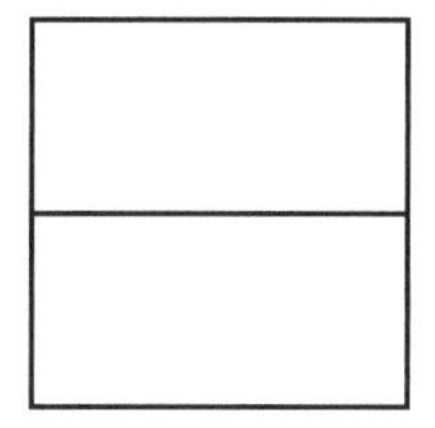

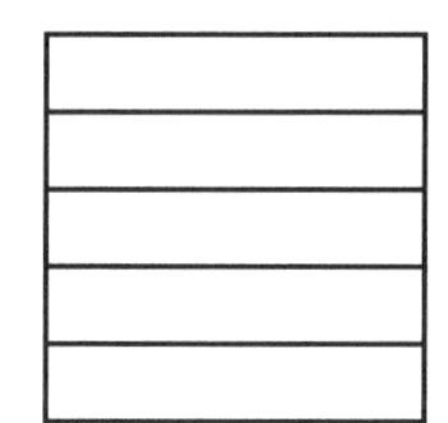

Solution: ____________ $\frac{1}{2}$ of the practice time is spent playing a game.

Explain how you got your answer.

____

____

____

Lesson 11 COMPARE FRACTIONS

PART ONE: Learn About Comparing Fractions

How can models help you compare fractions to each other?

Explore

You can **compare** a fraction to 0, $\frac{1}{2}$, and 1.

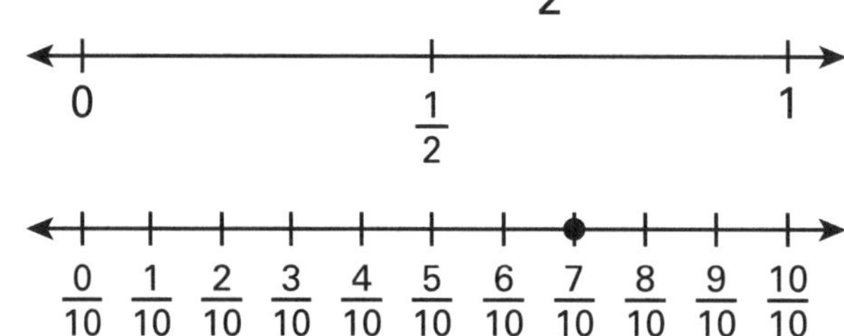

$\frac{7}{10} > 0$ $\frac{7}{10} > \frac{1}{2}$ $\frac{7}{10} < 1$

How can you tell if a fraction is **greater than** or **less than** another fraction?

Think

Look at the models.

Are they the same size and shape? yes

What fraction of model A is shaded? $\frac{3}{5}$

What fraction of model B is shaded? $\frac{2}{8}$

Which model has more shading? A

A  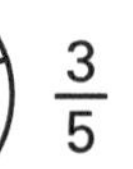

B 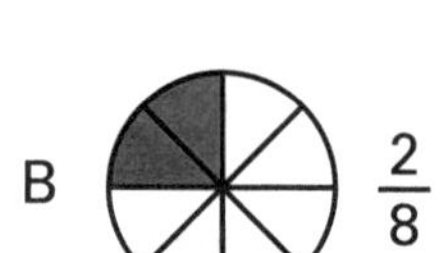

Connect

You can use the models to compare $\frac{3}{5}$ and $\frac{2}{8}$.
Model A has more shading than model B.
$\frac{3}{5}$ names a larger amount of the whole than $\frac{2}{8}$.
So, $\frac{3}{5}$ is greater than $\frac{2}{8}$.

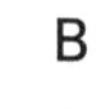

A 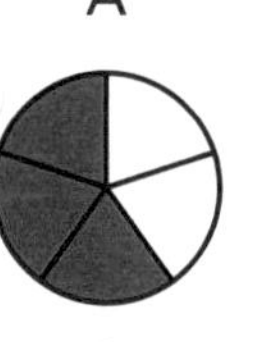 B 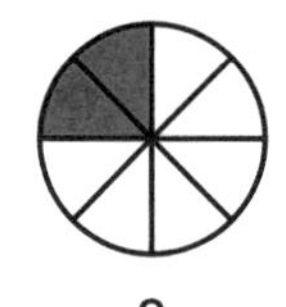

$\frac{3}{5} > \frac{2}{8}$

Let's Talk

Use the tenths model above to compare $\frac{1}{10}$ and $\frac{3}{10}$, and $\frac{7}{10}$ and $\frac{3}{10}$. Explain how to compare fractions with the same denominator.

Fill in the blanks. Solve the problem.

Josiah used $\frac{3}{4}$ yard of fabric for his art project. Keshawn used $\frac{2}{5}$ yard of fabric. Who used more fabric?

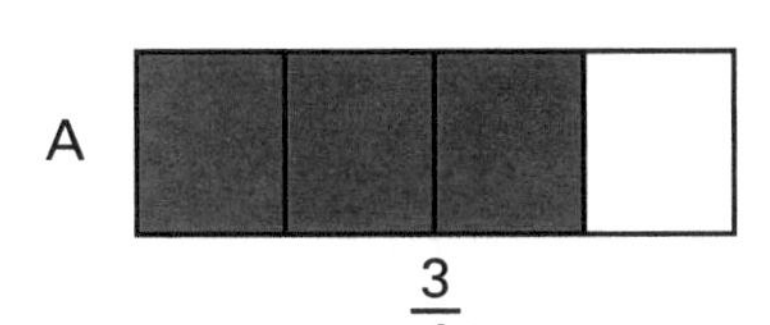

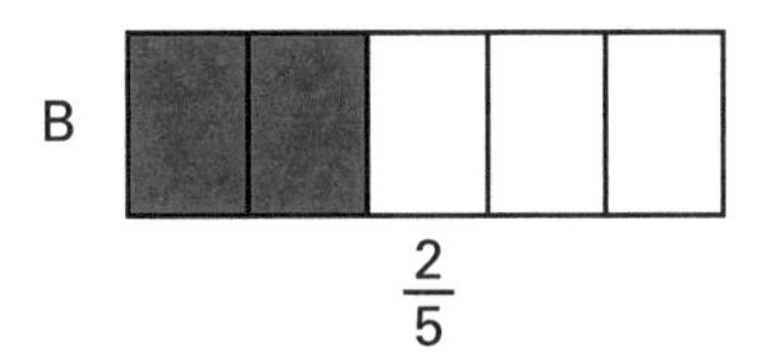

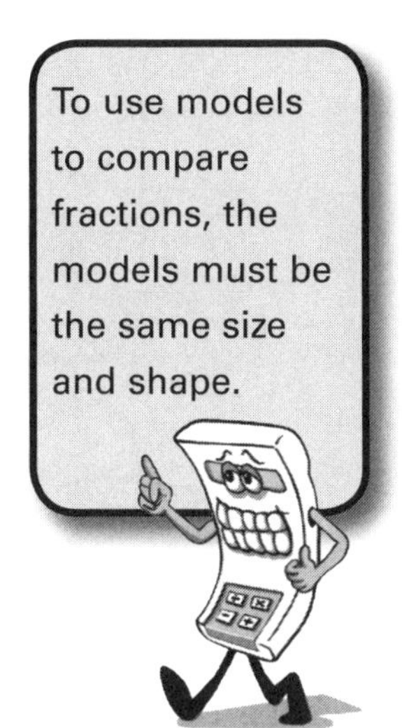

- Use the models to compare $\frac{3}{4}$ and $\frac{2}{5}$.
- Which figure has more shading? _______
- Which fraction is greater? _______

_______ $>$ _______

Solution: _______________ used more fabric.

Your Turn **Now, use what you know to solve this problem.**

1. Devin and Nancy are having veggie burgers for lunch. Devin has eaten $\frac{1}{3}$ of his burger. Nancy has eaten $\frac{5}{6}$ of her burger. Which is true?

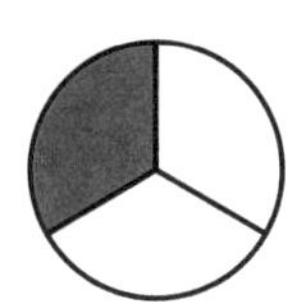

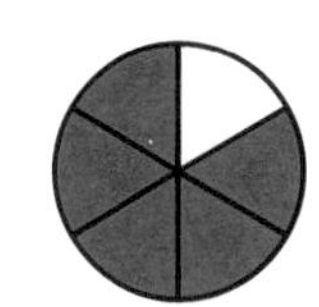

Ⓐ $\frac{1}{3} > \frac{5}{6}$ Ⓒ $\frac{1}{3} = \frac{5}{6}$

Ⓑ $\frac{5}{6} < \frac{1}{3}$ Ⓓ $\frac{5}{6} > \frac{1}{3}$

PART TWO: Learn More About Comparing Fractions

How can you compare fractions with the same numerator?

Explore

Models help you compare fractions.

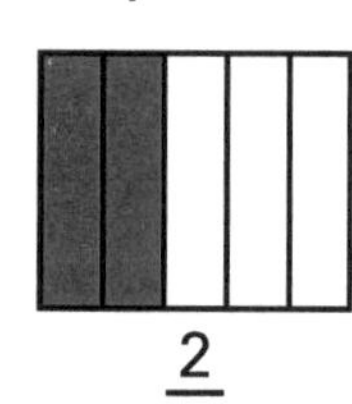

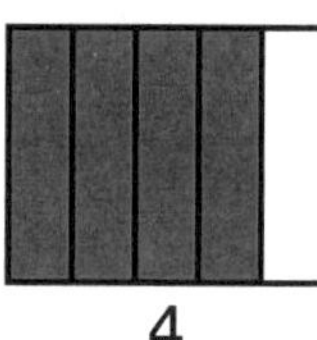

$\frac{2}{5} < \frac{4}{5}$

How can you compare fractions with the same **numerator** but different **denominators**?

Think

Look at the models.

Are they the same shape and size? yes

What fraction of model A is shaded? $\frac{1}{4}$

A
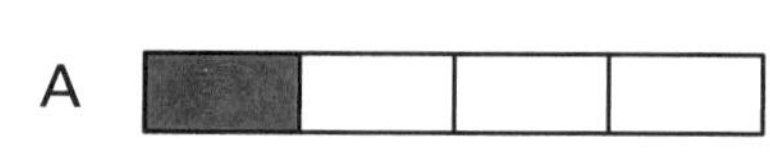

What fraction of model B is shaded? $\frac{1}{6}$

B
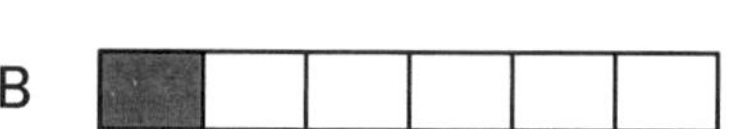

Which model has less shading? B

Which model is divided into more parts? B

Connect

The more parts a whole is divided into, the smaller the parts.
Sixths are smaller than fourths.
Both models have the same number of parts shaded: 1.
So, $\frac{1}{6}$ is less than $\frac{1}{4}$.

A
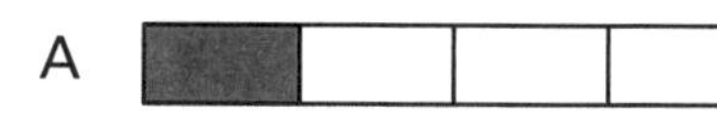

B

$\frac{1}{6} < \frac{1}{4}$

Let's Talk

Use the models for fourths and sixths. Which is greater, $\frac{3}{4}$ or $\frac{3}{6}$? Explain your answer.

Fill in the blanks. Solve the problem.

On Monday Julie walked $\frac{5}{8}$ of a mile. On Tuesday, she walked $\frac{5}{10}$ of a mile. On which day did Julie walk farther?

- Compare the models for $\frac{5}{8}$ and $\frac{5}{10}$.

A 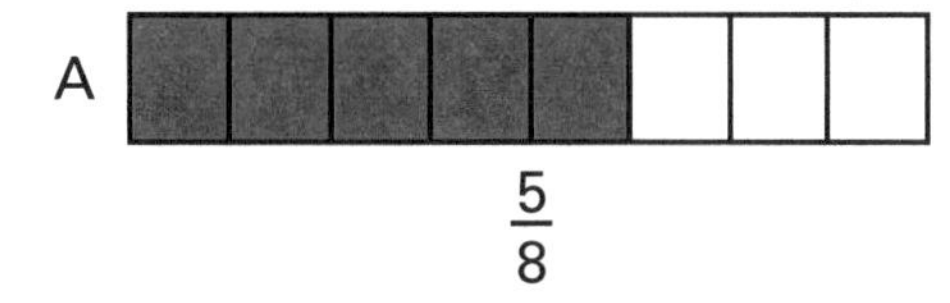

$\frac{5}{8}$

B 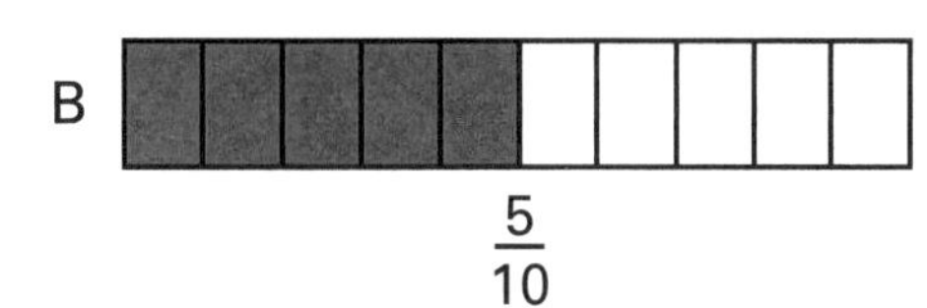

$\frac{5}{10}$

- How many eighths are shaded? _______

  How many tenths are shaded? _______

- Which are larger, eighths or tenths? _________

  Which model has less shading? _______

- Which is greater, 5 eighths or 5 tenths? _________

  _______ > _______

If numerators are the same, compare denominators. The fraction with the lesser denominator is the greater fraction.

Solution: Julie walked farther on __________.

Your Turn **Now, use what you know to solve this problem.**

2. Mr. Matheus cut a board $\frac{8}{10}$ foot long. Then he cut a wire $\frac{8}{12}$ foot long. Which is shorter, the board or the wire?

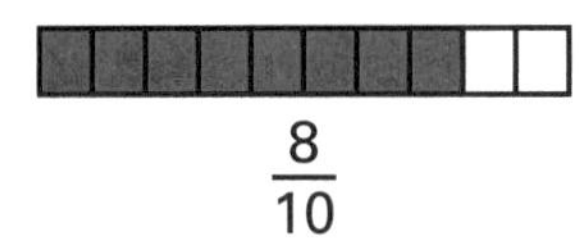

$\frac{8}{10}$

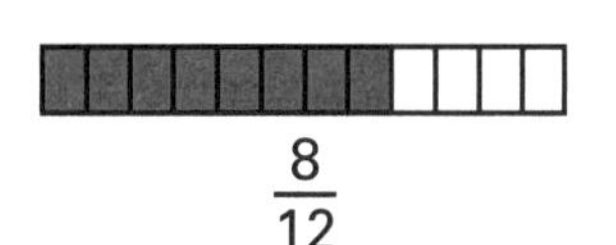

$\frac{8}{12}$

The __________ is shorter.

Solve the problem. Then read why each answer choice is correct or not correct.

Solve

Henry is baking cookies. He uses $\frac{3}{4}$ cup flour and $\frac{3}{5}$ cup sugar.

1 whole				
$\frac{1}{4}$	$\frac{1}{4}$	$\frac{1}{4}$	$\frac{1}{4}$	
$\frac{1}{5}$	$\frac{1}{5}$	$\frac{1}{5}$	$\frac{1}{5}$	$\frac{1}{5}$

Which is true?

Ⓐ $\frac{3}{4} = \frac{3}{5}$

Ⓑ $\frac{3}{5} < \frac{3}{4}$

Ⓒ $\frac{3}{4} < \frac{3}{5}$

Ⓓ $\frac{3}{5} > \frac{3}{4}$

Check

Check to see if you chose the correct answer.

The numerators are the same, so compare denominators. Fifths are smaller than fourths, so 3 fifths is less than 3 fourths.

So, $\frac{3}{5} < \frac{3}{4}$.

The correct answer is Ⓑ.

Why are the other answer choices not correct?

Ⓐ $\frac{3}{4} = \frac{3}{5}$	Fifths and fourths are not the same size, so 3 fifths and 3 fourths do not name the same amount.
Ⓒ $\frac{3}{4} < \frac{3}{5}$	Fourths are larger than fifths, so 3 fourths is not less than 3 fifths.
Ⓓ $\frac{3}{5} > \frac{3}{4}$	Fifths are smaller than fourths, so 3 fifths is not greater than 3 fourths.

Your Turn **Solve each problem. Use the hints to avoid mistakes.**

- Decide which model shows more shading or which fraction bar is longer.
- If fractions have the same denominator, compare numerators. The greater fraction has the greater numerator.
- If fractions have the same numerators, compare denominators. The greater fraction has the lesser denominator.

3. Mandy made two pans of banana bread. She gave some bread to her friends.

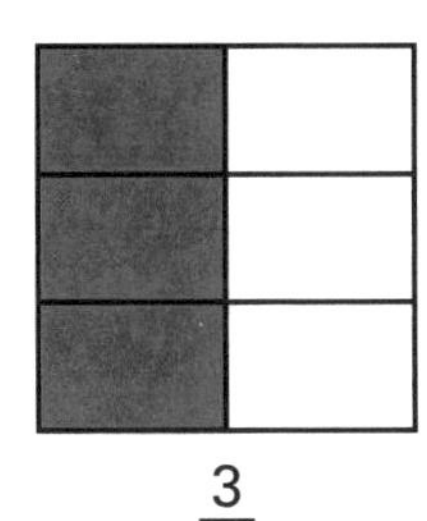

$\frac{3}{6}$

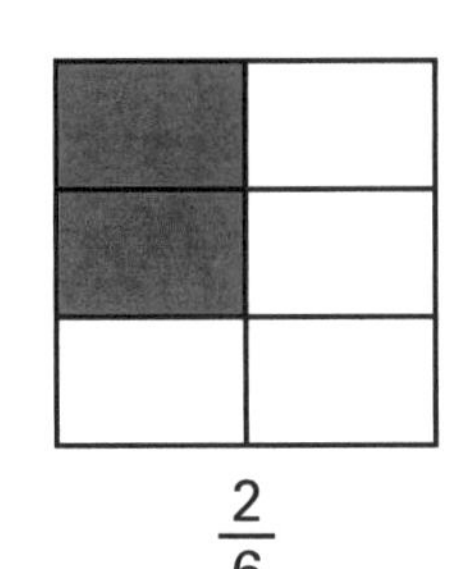

$\frac{2}{6}$

Which is true?

Ⓐ $\frac{3}{6} < \frac{2}{6}$

Ⓑ $\frac{2}{6} = \frac{3}{6}$

Ⓒ $\frac{2}{6} > \frac{3}{6}$

Ⓓ $\frac{2}{6} < \frac{3}{6}$

4. Stephan colored $\frac{6}{8}$ of one square blue. He colored $\frac{3}{4}$ of another square yellow.

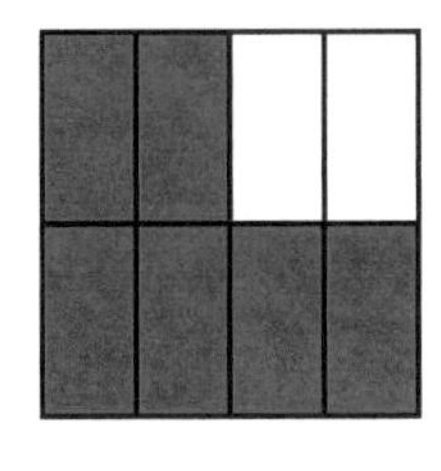

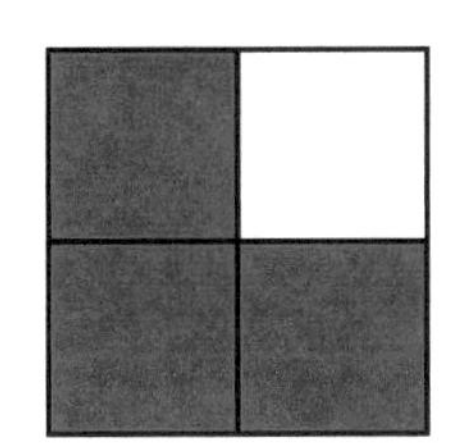

Which is true?

Ⓐ $\frac{3}{4} > \frac{6}{8}$

Ⓑ $\frac{3}{4} < \frac{6}{8}$

Ⓒ $\frac{6}{8} < \frac{3}{4}$

Ⓓ $\frac{6}{8} = \frac{3}{4}$

5. Tyler drew these circles with sidewalk chalk.

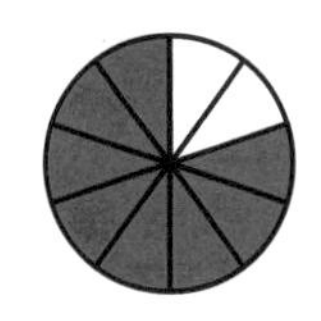

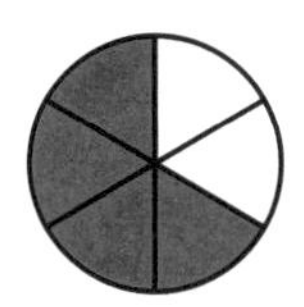

Which is true?

Ⓐ $\frac{8}{10} < \frac{4}{6}$

Ⓑ $\frac{8}{10} > \frac{4}{6}$

Ⓒ $\frac{4}{6} = \frac{8}{10}$

Ⓓ $\frac{4}{6} > \frac{8}{10}$

6. Which is true?

1 whole				
$\frac{1}{2}$		$\frac{1}{2}$		
$\frac{1}{3}$	$\frac{1}{3}$	$\frac{1}{3}$		

Ⓐ $\frac{1}{3} > \frac{1}{2}$

Ⓑ $\frac{1}{2} < \frac{1}{3}$

Ⓒ $\frac{1}{3} < \frac{1}{2}$

Ⓓ $\frac{1}{2} = \frac{1}{3}$

PART FOUR: Write the Best Answer

Study the model. It is a good example of a written answer.

Student Model

Show

Susanna and Rachel were eating sandwiches that were the same size. Susanna ate $\frac{1}{4}$ of her sandwich. Rachel ate $\frac{2}{6}$ of her sandwich. Who ate more of her sandwich? Use pictures, words, or numbers to show your work.

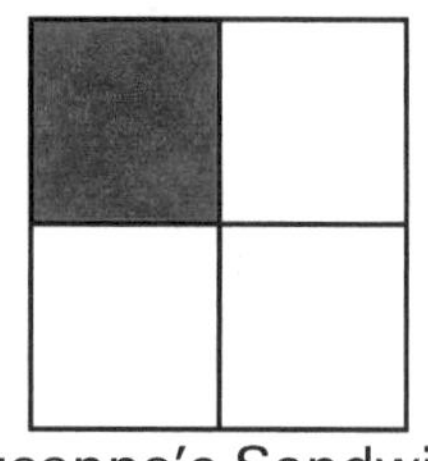

Susanna's Sandwich

$\frac{1}{4}$

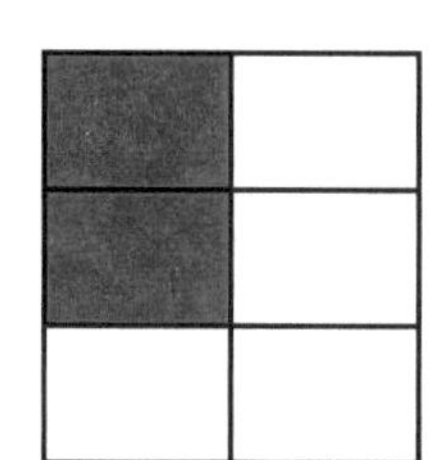

Rachel's Sandwich

$\frac{2}{6}$

$\frac{2}{6} > \frac{1}{4}$

Solution: Rachel ate more of her sandwich.

☑ The student shows each step.

☑ The student correctly answers the question asked.

Explain

Explain how you got your answer.

I shaded the models to show the amount of each sandwich that was eaten. Susanna ate $\frac{1}{4}$ of her sandwich, so I shaded 1 of the 4 equal parts. Rachel ate $\frac{2}{6}$ of her sandwich, so I shaded 2 of the 6 equal parts. I compared the models and saw the $\frac{2}{6}$ model has more shading, so $\frac{2}{6}$ is greater than $\frac{1}{4}$. Rachel ate more of her sandwich than Susanna.

☑ The student gives important details about how to compare the fractions.

☑ The student uses the math words *equal parts, compare,* and *greater than.*

Your Turn **Solve the problem. Use what you learned from the model.**

7. Shanaya fills $\frac{4}{6}$ of a pitcher with water. She fills $\frac{7}{8}$ of a pitcher with lemonade. The pitchers are the same size. Does Shanaya have less water or lemonade?

Use pictures, words, or numbers to show your work.

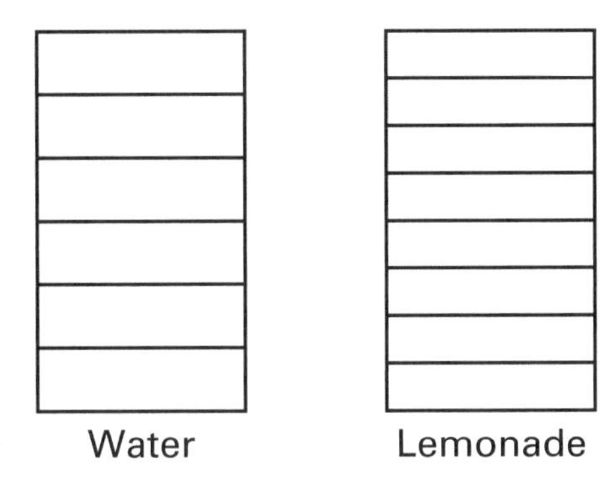

CHECKLIST

Did you . . .

- ☐ show each step?
- ☐ answer the question asked?
- ☐ give important details?
- ☐ use math words?

Solution: Shanaya has less ________________.

Explain how you got your answer.

____

____

____

____

____

____

As you solve comparing fraction problems, you may want to:
- use models to compare the fractions.
- pay careful attention to numerators and denominators:
  - if the denominators are the same, look for the greater numerator to find the greater fraction.
  - if the numerators are the same, look for the lesser denominator to find the greater fraction.

Solve each problem.

8. Which is true?

1 whole					
$\frac{1}{5}$	$\frac{1}{5}$	$\frac{1}{5}$	$\frac{1}{5}$	$\frac{1}{5}$	
$\frac{1}{6}$	$\frac{1}{6}$	$\frac{1}{6}$	$\frac{1}{6}$	$\frac{1}{6}$	$\frac{1}{6}$

Ⓐ $\frac{4}{6} = \frac{3}{5}$

Ⓑ $\frac{3}{5} > \frac{4}{6}$

Ⓒ $\frac{3}{6} < \frac{4}{5}$

Ⓓ $\frac{4}{6} < \frac{3}{5}$

9. Latisha's garden is $\frac{5}{6}$ full of petunias. Mark's garden is $\frac{5}{8}$ full of pansies. The gardens are the same size.

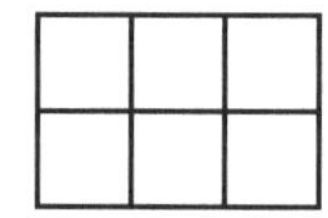 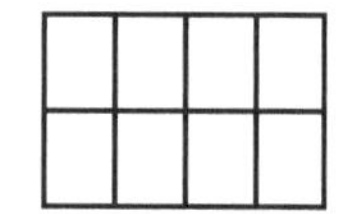

Which is true?

Ⓐ $\frac{5}{6} > \frac{5}{8}$

Ⓑ $\frac{5}{6} < \frac{5}{8}$

Ⓒ $\frac{5}{8} = \frac{5}{6}$

Ⓓ $\frac{5}{8} > \frac{5}{6}$

10. Newspaper covers $\frac{3}{4}$ of Cheryl's birdcage and $\frac{5}{8}$ of Andy's birdcage.

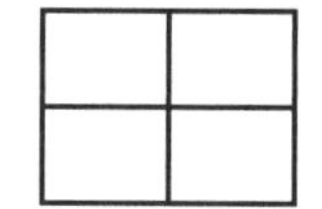 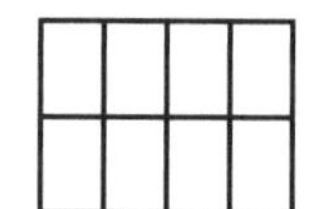

Which is true?

Ⓐ Cheryl's birdcage has more newspaper.

Ⓑ Andy's birdcage has more newspaper.

Ⓒ Both birdcages have the same amount of newspaper.

Ⓓ Cheryl's birdcage has less newspaper.

11. Dasan collects trains. He stores his trains in a plastic case. The left side of the case is $\frac{9}{10}$ full. The right side of the case is $\frac{5}{10}$ full. Which is true?

Ⓐ $\frac{9}{10} < \frac{5}{10}$

Ⓑ $\frac{9}{10} = \frac{5}{10}$

Ⓒ $\frac{5}{10} > \frac{9}{10}$

Ⓓ $\frac{5}{10} < \frac{9}{10}$

12. $\frac{2}{4}$ of Ben's books are chapter books and $\frac{2}{5}$ are picture books. Which is true?

Ⓐ Ben has more picture books than chapter books.

Ⓑ Ben has fewer chapter books than picture books.

Ⓒ Ben has the same number of picture books as chapter books.

Ⓓ Ben has more chapter books than picture books.

13. Marion spent $\frac{3}{8}$ hour playing a game. She spent $\frac{3}{6}$ hour doing her homework. Which is true?

Ⓐ $\frac{3}{8} < \frac{3}{6}$

Ⓑ $\frac{3}{6} = \frac{3}{8}$

Ⓒ $\frac{3}{6} < \frac{3}{8}$

Ⓓ $\frac{3}{8} > \frac{3}{6}$

14. Salimah used $\frac{4}{6}$ teaspoon of salt in a recipe. She used $\frac{5}{8}$ teaspoon of baking powder.

Shade the models to show $\frac{4}{6}$ and $\frac{5}{8}$.

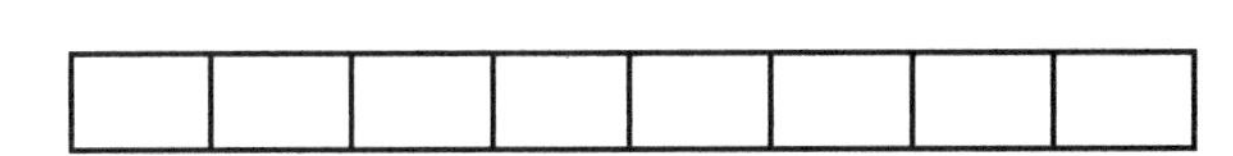

Use the models to compare $\frac{4}{6}$ and $\frac{5}{8}$. Write $>$, $<$, or $=$.

$\frac{4}{6}$ ___ $\frac{5}{8}$

15. Jude and Bill made spinners for a game. Jude colored $\frac{2}{10}$ of his spinner red. Bill colored $\frac{3}{8}$ of his spinner red. Who colored more of his spinner red?

Use pictures, words, or numbers to show your work.

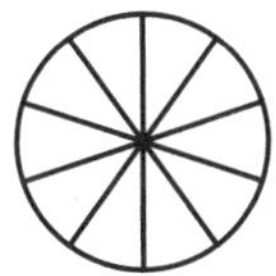

Solution: _________ colored more of his spinner red.

Explain how you got your answer.

___

___

___

___

Lesson 12 FRACTIONS GREATER THAN 1

PART ONE: Learn About Fractions Greater Than 1

How can models show fractions greater than 1?

Explore

A **fraction** is equal to 1 when its **numerator** and **denominator** are the same.

$\frac{1}{3}$	$\frac{1}{3}$	$\frac{1}{3}$

numerator → 3, denominator → 3: $\frac{3}{3} = 1$

How can you show amounts greater than 1 whole?

Think

$\frac{1}{3}$	$\frac{1}{3}$	$\frac{1}{3}$

$\frac{3}{3}$ = 1 whole

$\frac{1}{3}$	$\frac{1}{3}$	$\frac{1}{3}$

$\frac{3}{3}$ = 1 whole

$\frac{1}{3}$	$\frac{1}{3}$	$\frac{1}{3}$

$\frac{1}{3}$

The model shows each whole divided into thirds.

There are 7 thirds shaded in all.

The model also shows 2 wholes plus 1 third shaded.

Connect

7 thirds = $\frac{7}{3}$

$\frac{7}{3}$ is an **improper fraction**.

An improper fraction has a numerator that is greater than or equal to its denominator.

2 wholes and 1 third = $2 + \frac{1}{3} = 2\frac{1}{3}$

$2\frac{1}{3}$ is a **mixed number**.

A mixed number has a whole-number part and a fraction part.

$\frac{7}{3}$ and $2\frac{1}{3}$ name the same amount, so $\frac{7}{3} = 2\frac{1}{3}$.

Improper fractions and mixed numbers are two ways to show amounts greater than 1 whole.

Let's Talk

How are $\frac{7}{3}$ and $2\frac{1}{3}$ different? How are they the same?

Fill in the blanks. Solve the problem.

Jamal used $2\frac{1}{4}$ cups of water to make apple juice.
What is this number written as an improper fraction?

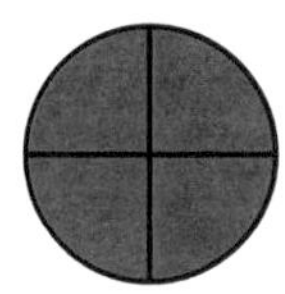
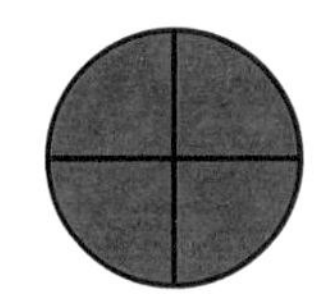
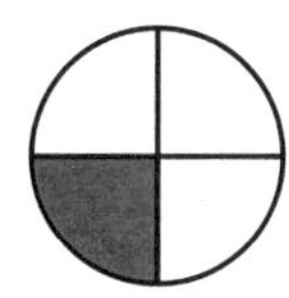

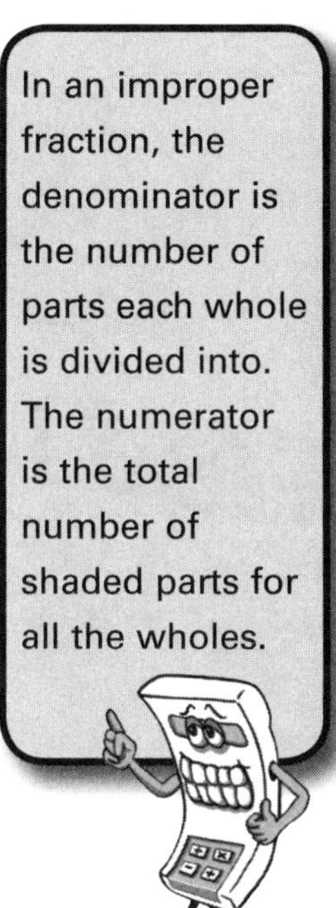

- Find the denominator.

  This model shows each whole divided into ________.

  The denominator of the improper fraction is ______.

- Find the numerator.

  There are ______ fourths shaded in all.

  The numerator of the improper fraction is ______.

- Write the improper fraction. $\frac{\square}{\square}$

Solution: $2\frac{1}{4} = \frac{\square}{\square}$

Your Turn **Now, use what you know to solve this problem.**

1. What is the missing number?

$5\frac{1}{2} = \frac{\square}{2}$

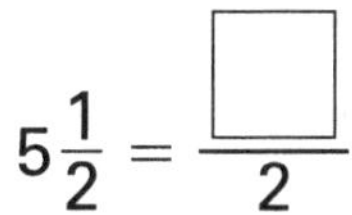

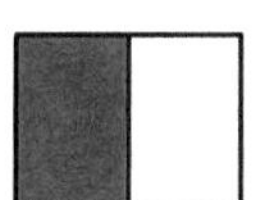

Ⓐ 5
Ⓑ 6
Ⓒ 11
Ⓓ 12

How can a number line show fractions greater than 1?

Explore

You can show fractions less than and equal to 1 on a number line.

How can you show mixed numbers and improper fractions on a number line?

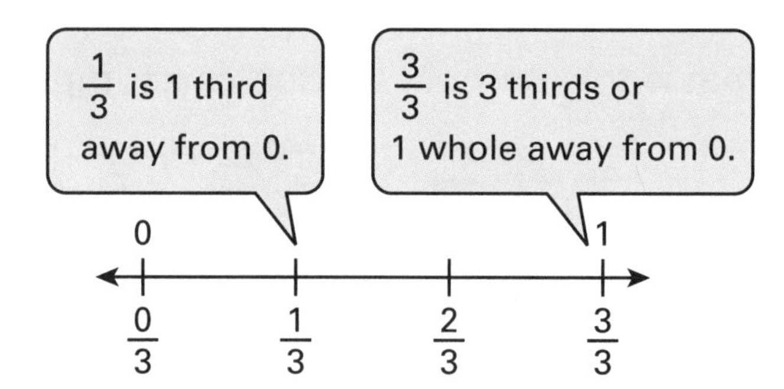

Think

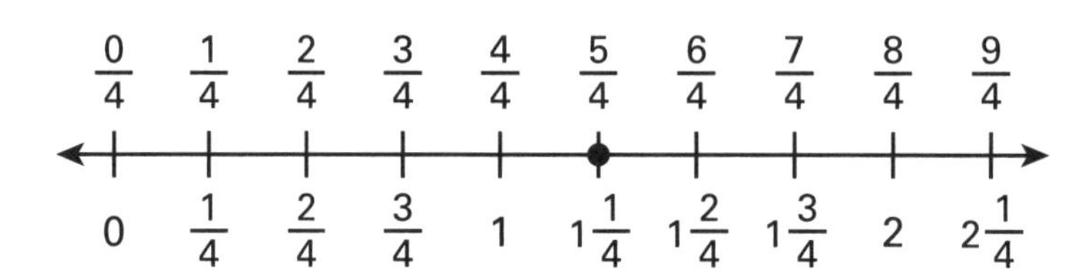

On the number line, each whole is divided into fourths.

The point is 5 fourths away from 0.

The point is also 1 whole plus 1 fourth away from 0.

Connect

5 fourths $= \frac{5}{4} \leftarrow$ **improper fraction**

1 whole and 1 fourth $= 1\frac{1}{4} \leftarrow$ **mixed number**

$\frac{5}{4}$ and $1\frac{1}{4}$ are the same distance from 0, so $\frac{5}{4} = 1\frac{1}{4}$.

A number line is a good way to show fractions less than, equal to, and greater than 1.

Let's Talk

What would be the next 4 numbers above the number line in **Think**? What would be the next 4 numbers below the number line?

Fill in the blanks. Solve the problem.

Haley's pet fish is $2\frac{2}{3}$ inches long. What is this number written as an improper fraction? Use the number line to help you.

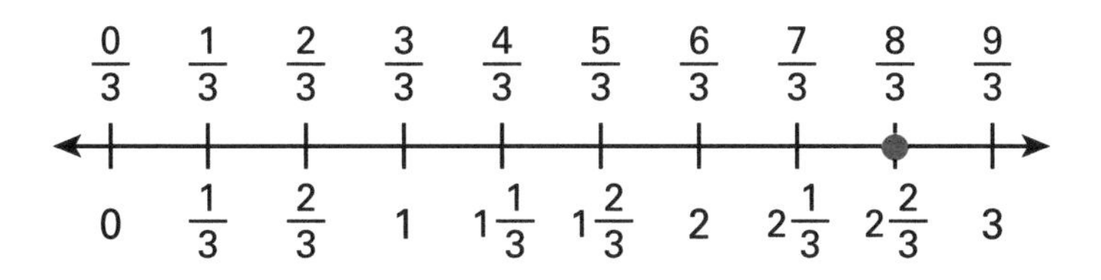

- Each whole on the number line is divided into __________.

- Place a point on the number line at $2\frac{2}{3}$.

  The point is _______ wholes plus _______ thirds away from 0.

  The point is also _______ thirds away from 0.

- Write the improper fraction. 8 thirds = $\frac{\square}{\square}$

Solution: $2\frac{2}{3} = \frac{\square}{\square}$

Your Turn **Now, use what you know to solve this problem.**

2. Use the number line to write $\frac{8}{6}$ as a mixed number.

$\frac{0}{6}$ $\frac{1}{6}$ $\frac{2}{6}$ $\frac{3}{6}$ $\frac{4}{6}$ $\frac{5}{6}$ $\frac{6}{6}$ $\frac{7}{6}$ $\frac{8}{6}$ $\frac{9}{6}$

0 $\frac{1}{6}$ $\frac{2}{6}$ $\frac{3}{6}$ $\frac{4}{6}$ $\frac{5}{6}$ 1 $1\frac{1}{6}$ $1\frac{2}{6}$ $1\frac{3}{6}$

$\frac{8}{6} = \square\frac{\square}{\square}$

Solve the problem. Then read why each answer choice is correct or not correct.

Solve

Diego's younger brother is $1\frac{3}{4}$ years old. Which model could be used to show his brother's age?

 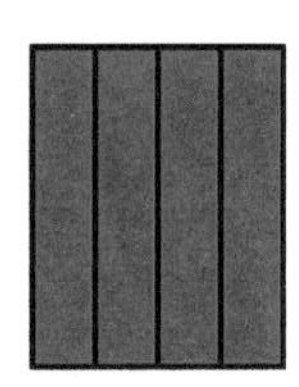 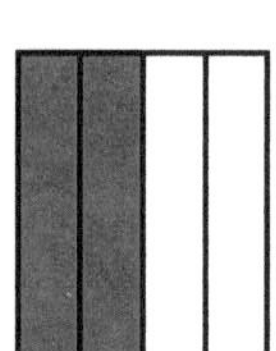

Ⓒ 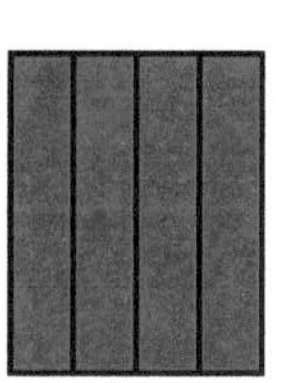 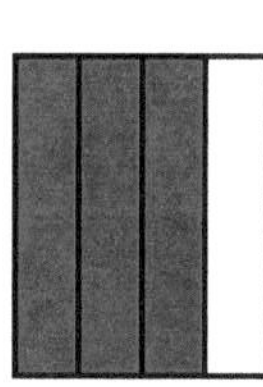

Ⓑ 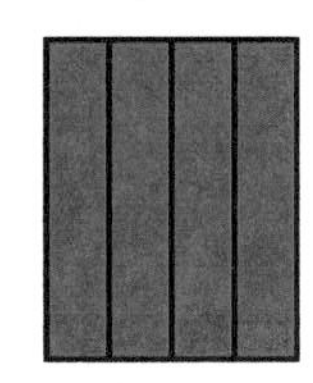 

Ⓓ 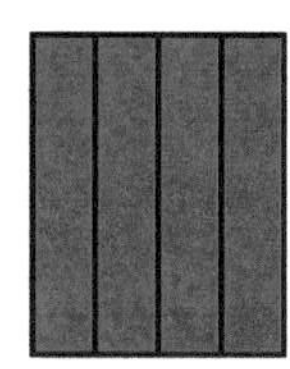 

Check

Check to see if you chose the correct answer.

$1\frac{3}{4}$ is the same as 1 whole plus $\frac{3}{4}$, or $1 + \frac{3}{4}$.

The model should show 1 whole and 3 fourths shaded.

So, the correct answer is Ⓒ.

Why are the other answer choices not correct?

Ⓐ 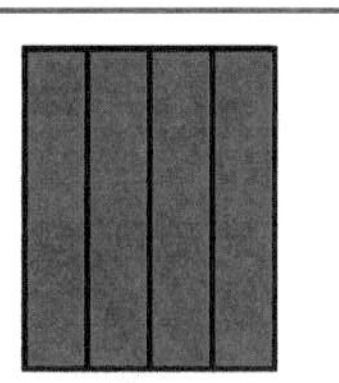	This model shows 1 whole and $\frac{2}{4}$, or $1\frac{2}{4}$.
Ⓑ 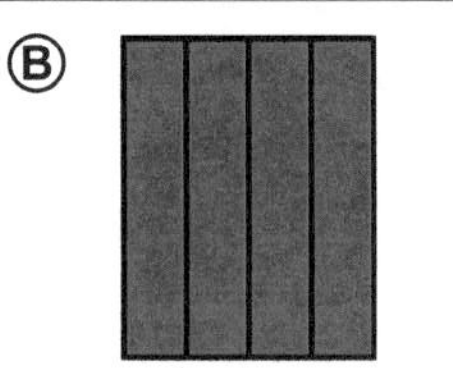	This model shows 2 wholes. Each whole is divided into fourths, and all the fourths are shaded.
Ⓓ 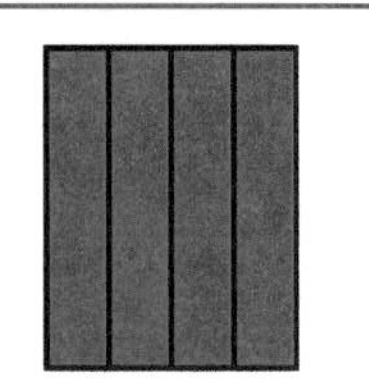 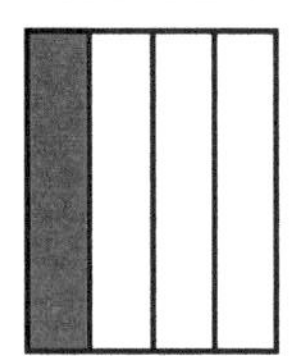	This model shows 1 whole and $\frac{1}{4}$, or $1\frac{1}{4}$.

Your Turn **Solve each problem. Use the hints to avoid mistakes.**

- On a model, carefully count the total number of shaded parts and the number of parts each whole is divided into.
- On a number line, carefully count how many wholes and parts a point is away from 0.
- Remember that the denominator is the number of parts each whole is divided into. It is not the total number of parts for all the wholes.

3. Which fraction is shown by the model?

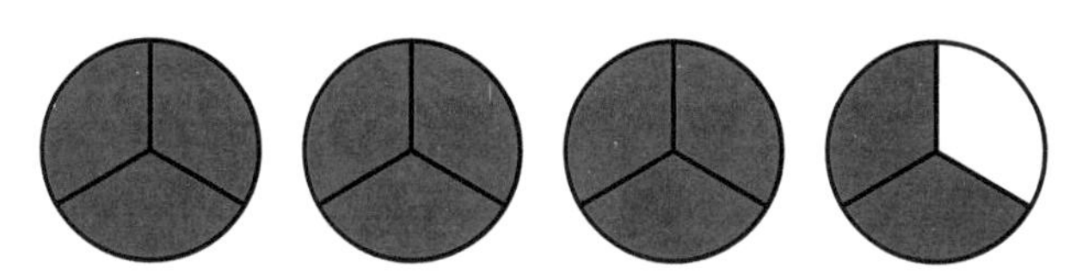

Ⓐ $\frac{11}{12}$

Ⓑ $\frac{11}{3}$

Ⓒ $\frac{12}{3}$

Ⓓ $\frac{3}{3}$

4. Which number line shows $1\frac{1}{6}$?

Ⓐ 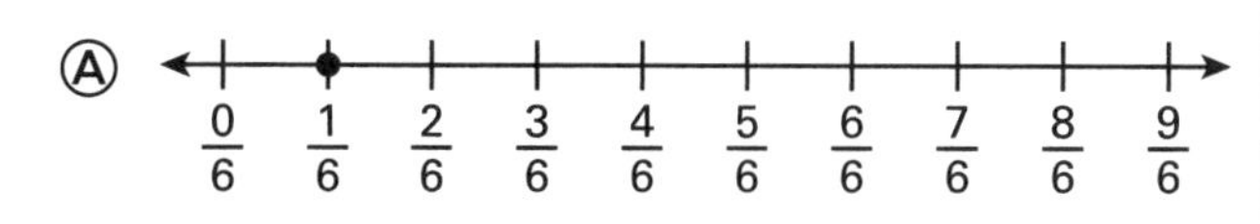

Ⓑ 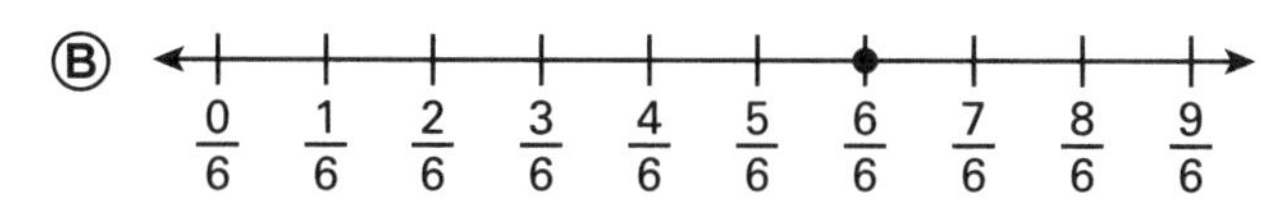

Ⓒ 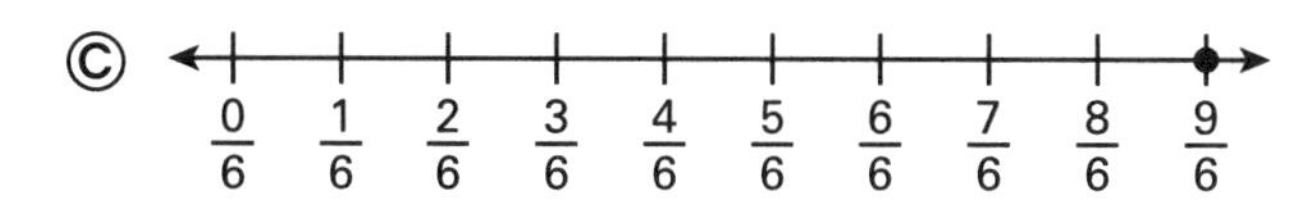

Ⓓ 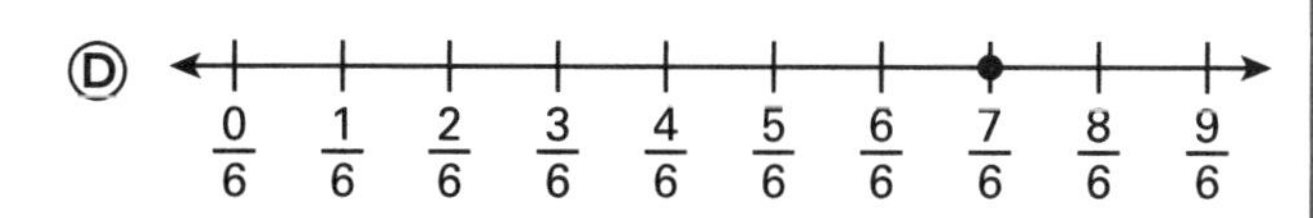

5. What is $\frac{12}{8}$ written as a mixed number?

Use the number line to help you.

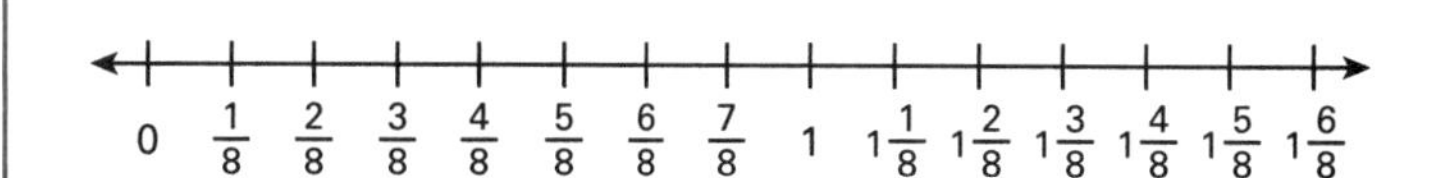

Ⓐ $\frac{4}{8}$

Ⓑ $\frac{8}{12}$

Ⓒ $1\frac{3}{8}$

Ⓓ $1\frac{4}{8}$

6. Which model shows $\frac{12}{5}$?

Ⓐ 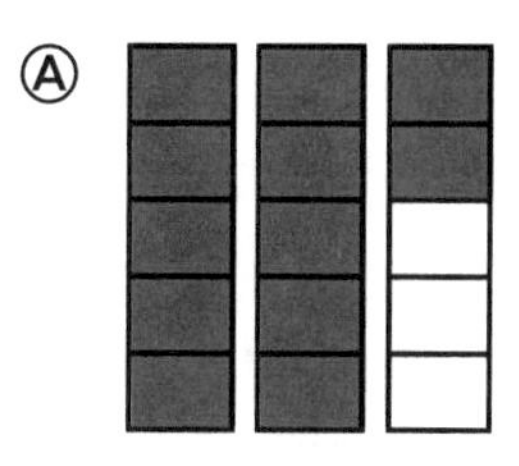

Ⓒ 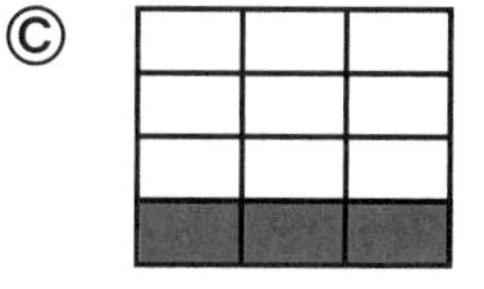

Ⓑ 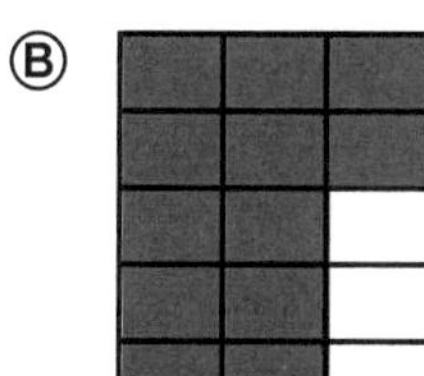

Ⓓ 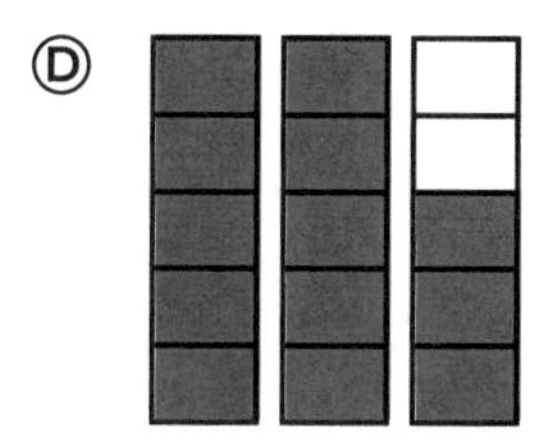

Study the model. It is a good example of a written answer.

Student Model

Show

Jaivon's new puppy weighs $4\frac{5}{8}$ pounds. What is the puppy's weight written as an improper fraction?

Use pictures, words, or numbers to show your work.

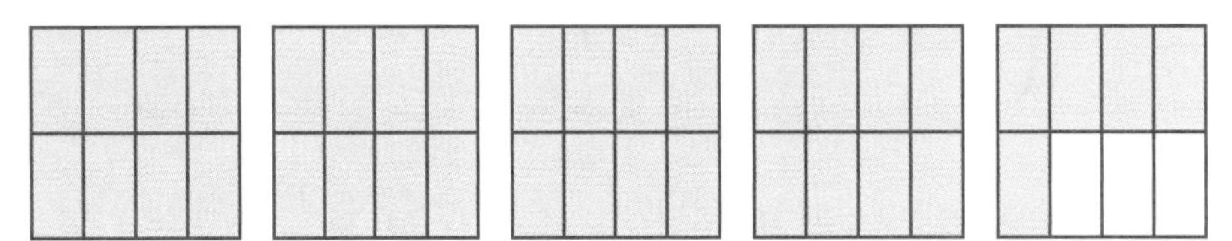

$4\frac{5}{8} = 4 + \frac{5}{8}$, so shade 4 wholes and 5 eighths.

There are 37 eighths shaded.

☑ The student shows each step.

Solution: $\frac{37}{8}$ pounds

☑ The student correctly answers the question asked.

Explain how you got your answer.

The fraction part of the mixed number has a denominator of 8, so I drew a model of wholes divided into eighths. I shaded the model to show 4 wholes and 5 eighths. Then I counted how many eighths were shaded in all. There were 37 eighths shaded in all. So, $4\frac{5}{8}$ written as an improper fraction is $\frac{37}{8}$.

☑ The student gives important details about how to write the improper fraction.

☑ The student uses the math words *mixed number, denominator, eighths,* and *improper fraction.*

Your Turn **Solve the problem. Use what you learned from the model.**

CHECKLIST

Did you . . .

- ☐ show each step?
- ☐ answer the question asked?
- ☐ give important details?
- ☐ use math words?

7. Jamie lives $\frac{13}{5}$ miles from school. What is this distance written as a mixed number?

Use pictures, words, or numbers to show your work.

Solution: ______ miles

Explain how you got your answer.

____

____

____

____

____

PART FIVE: Prepare for a Test

As you solve problems with fractions greater than 1, you may want to
- draw and shade a model to check your work.
- divide a number line into fractional parts and label each part. Include improper fractions and mixed numbers. Then place a point on the number line.

Solve each problem.

8. Leslie's kitchen table is $1\frac{3}{4}$ meters long. What is this number written as an improper fraction?

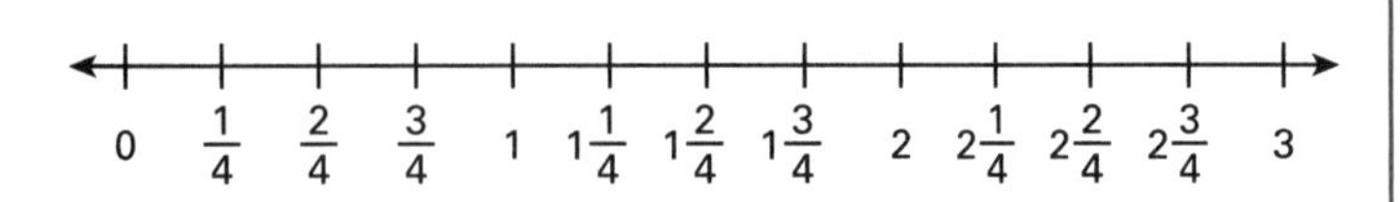

Ⓐ $\frac{3}{4}$

Ⓑ $\frac{7}{4}$

Ⓒ $\frac{5}{4}$

Ⓓ $\frac{9}{4}$

9. Which mixed number does the model show?

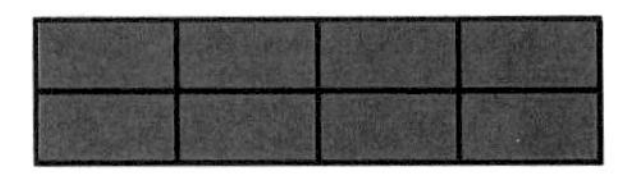
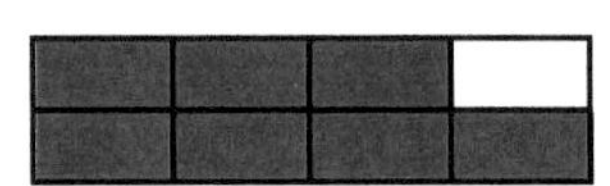

Ⓐ $1\frac{3}{8}$

Ⓑ $1\frac{9}{10}$

Ⓒ $1\frac{7}{8}$

Ⓓ $2\frac{1}{8}$

10. Which model shows $2\frac{2}{6}$?

Ⓐ 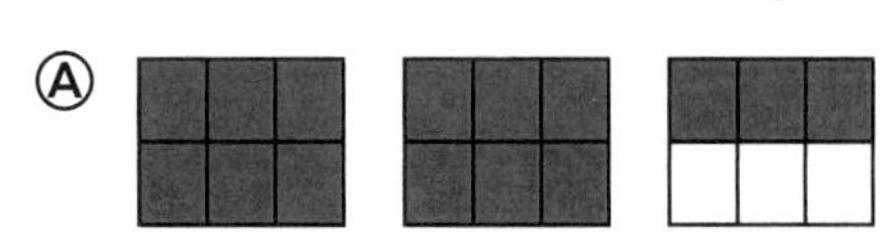

Ⓑ 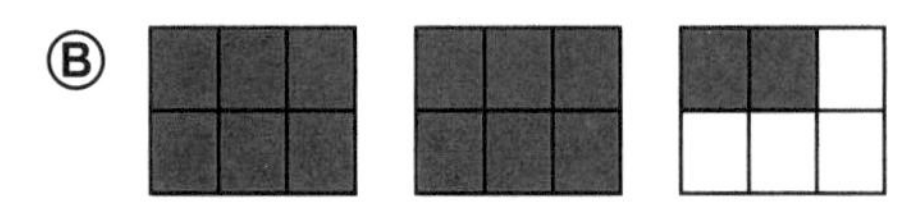

Ⓒ 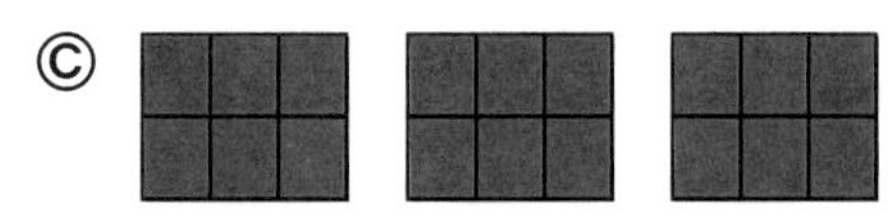

Ⓓ 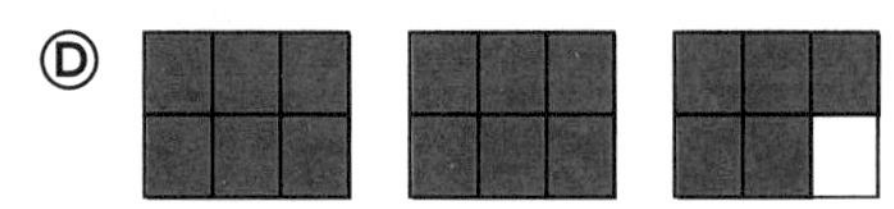

11. Which number line has a point at $2\frac{1}{4}$?

Ⓐ 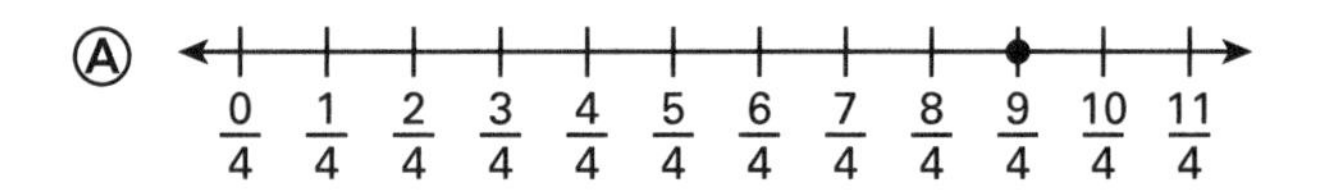

Ⓑ 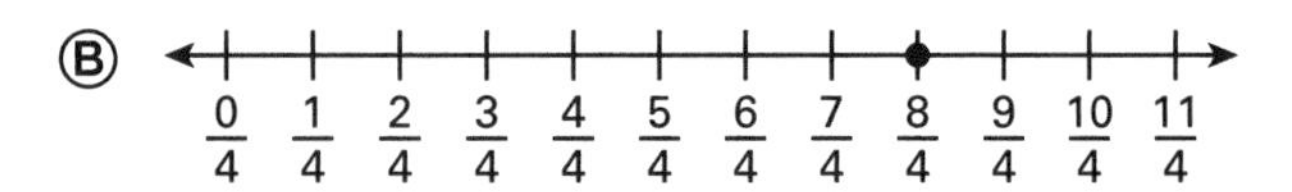

Ⓒ 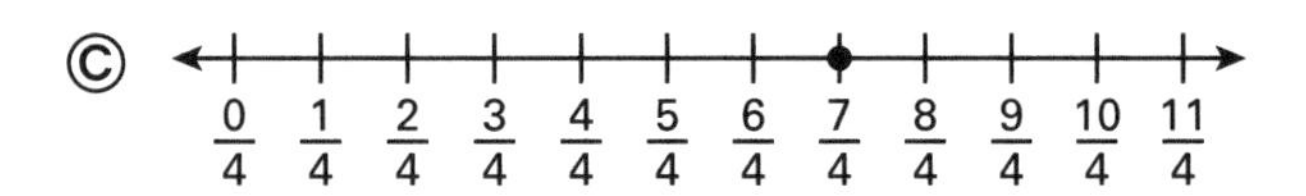

Ⓓ 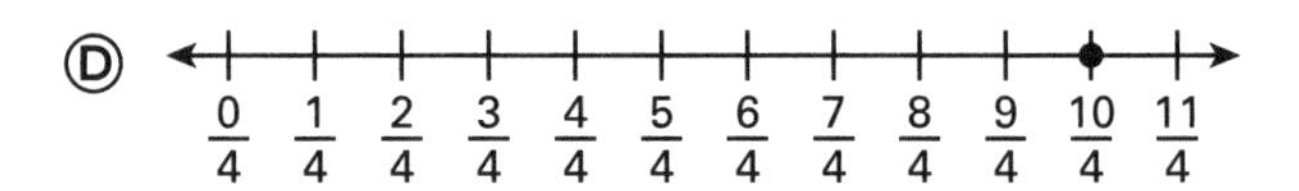

12. Jessica used a model to show her cat's age in years. How old is Jessica's cat?

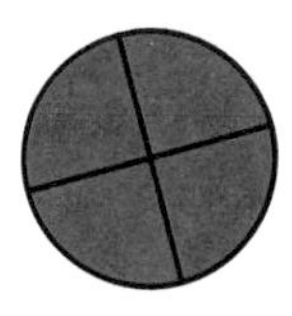 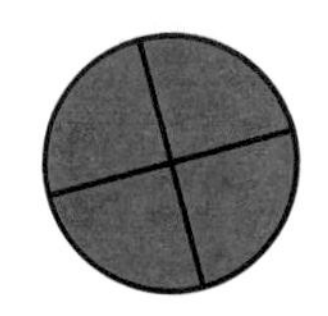 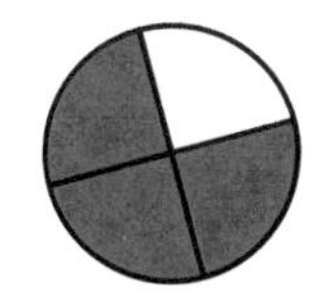

Ⓐ 2 years

Ⓑ $2\frac{3}{4}$ years

Ⓒ 3 years

Ⓓ $8\frac{3}{4}$ years

13. Which improper fraction does the point on the number line show?

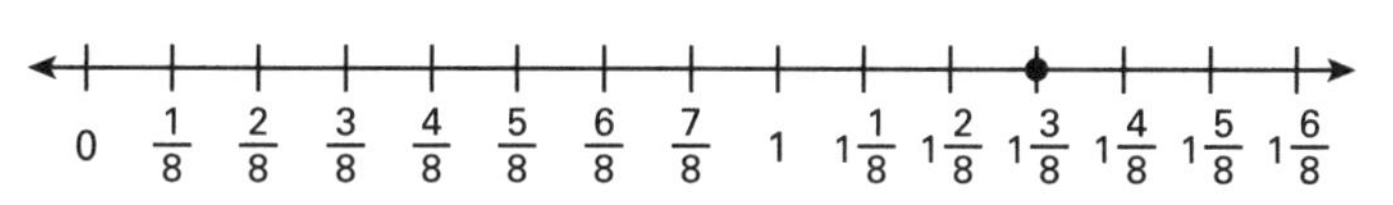

Ⓐ $\frac{3}{8}$

Ⓑ $\frac{8}{8}$

Ⓒ $\frac{10}{8}$

Ⓓ $\frac{11}{8}$

14. Draw a model to show $2\frac{4}{8}$.

Write the mixed number as an improper fraction.

$2\frac{4}{8}$ = ______

15. Sienna spent $2\frac{1}{5}$ hours working in her garden.

What is $2\frac{1}{5}$ written as an improper fraction?

Use pictures, words, or numbers to show your work.

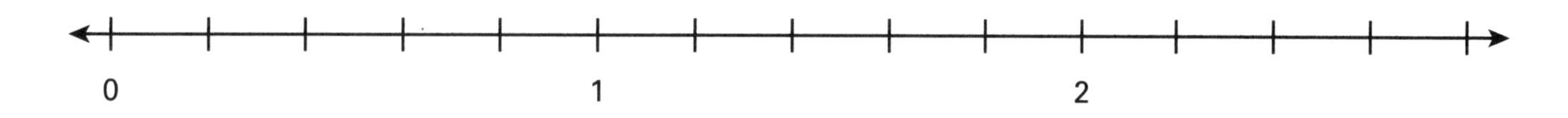

Solution: $2\frac{1}{5}$ = ______

Explain how you got your answer.

____

____

____

____

Lesson 13 PLANE FIGURES

PART ONE: Learn About Congruent Figures

How can you decide if figures are congruent?

Plane figures are flat, closed shapes. You can sort them by their number of **sides**.

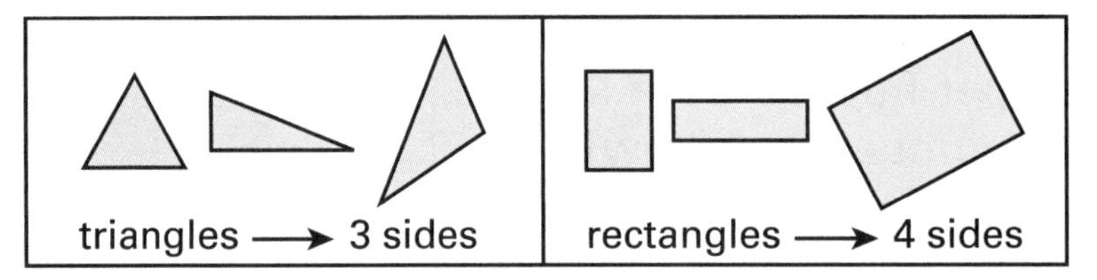

Plane figures with the same shape can have different sizes.
How can you describe plane figures that are the same shape and size?

Think

Look closely at figures A and B.

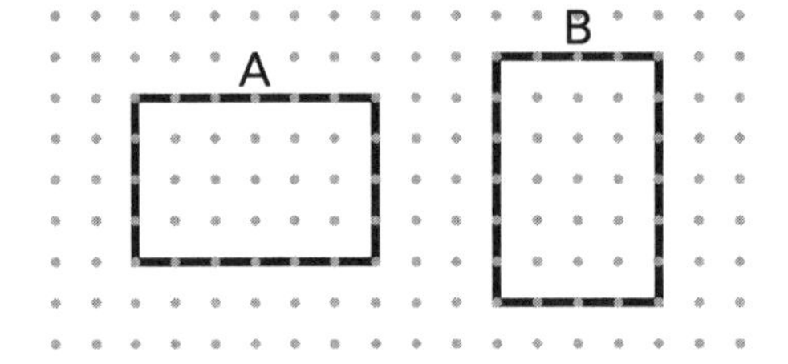

Are the figures the same shape? ___yes___
Are the long sides of both figures the same length? ___yes___
Are the short sides of both figures the same length? ___yes___

Connect

Figures A and B are the same shape and same size.
When figures are the same shape and size, they are **congruent**.
A is congruent to B.

Let's Talk

Put together A and B to make a larger rectangle. How tall is the rectangle? How wide is it? How tall and how wide would a congruent figure be?

Fill in the blanks. Solve the problem.

Beth and Lila each drew a figure on centimeter grid paper.

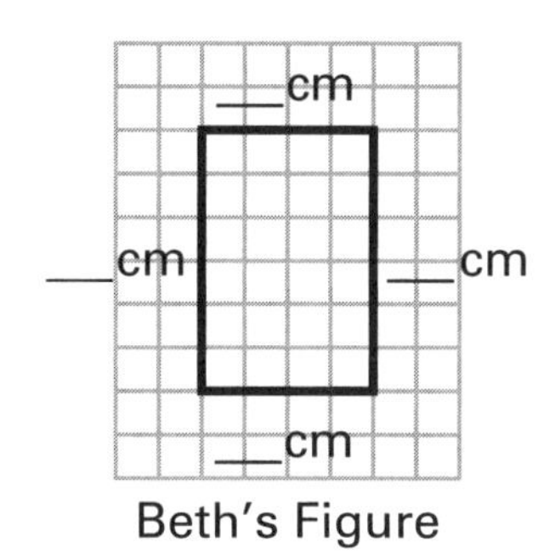

Beth's Figure

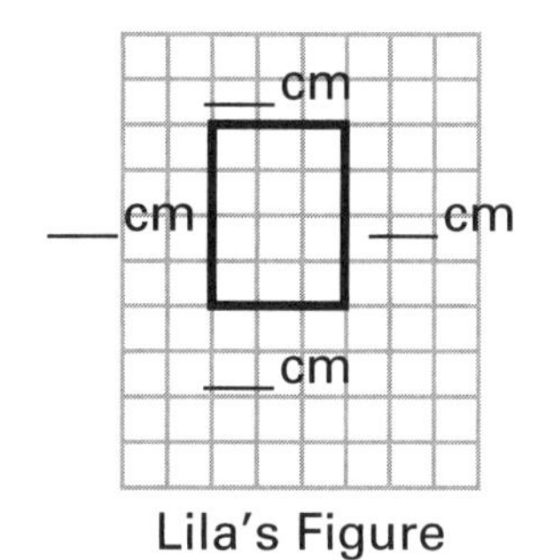

Lila's Figure

Are the figures congruent?

- Find the lengths of all four sides of each figure.
  Write the length of each side on the model.
  Are the figures the same shape? _______
  Are the figures the same size? _______
- Congruent figures are the same shape and size.
  Are the figures congruent? _______

Solution: The figures __________ congruent.

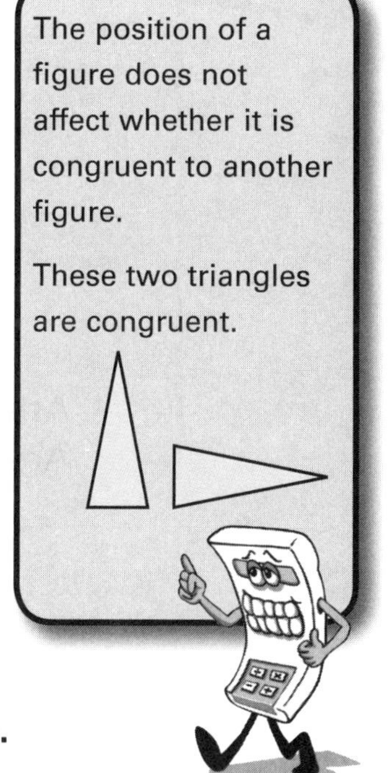

Now, use what you know to solve this problem.

1. Which figures are congruent?

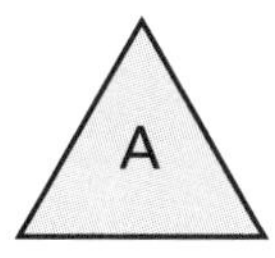

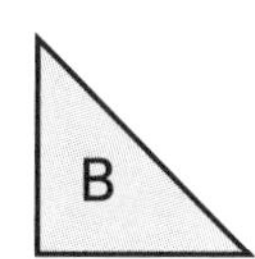

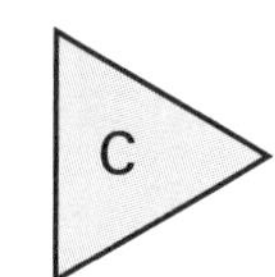

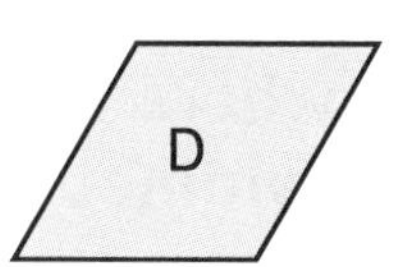

Ⓐ C and D
Ⓑ A and C
Ⓒ A, B, and C
Ⓓ A and B

How can you find out if figures have symmetry?

Explore

Congruent figures are the same shape and same size.

A and B are congruent figures.

How can you describe a figure that can be divided into two congruent parts?

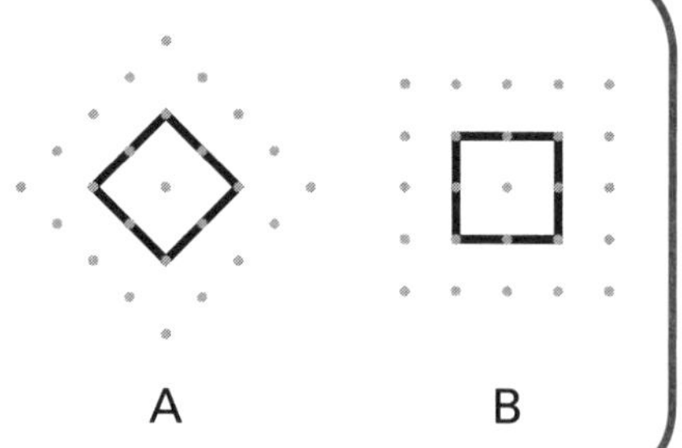

Think

This picture shows a figure being folded along a dotted line.

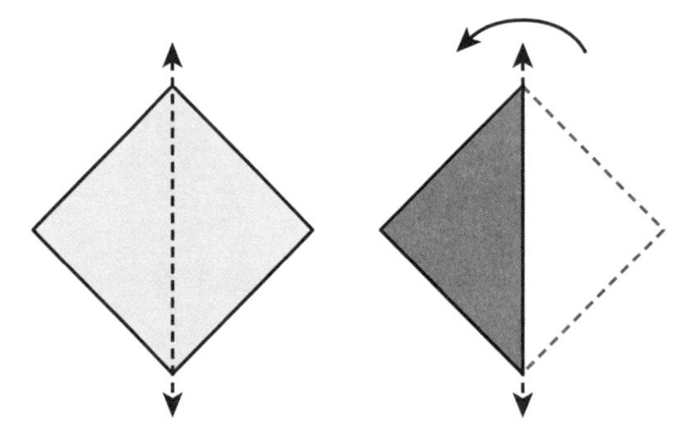

Are the two parts of the figure the same shape? yes
Are the two parts of the figure the same size? yes

Connect

The two parts of this figure are congruent.

If you can fold a figure along a line so that the two parts match exactly, the figure has **line symmetry**.

The line where you fold is called a **line of symmetry**.

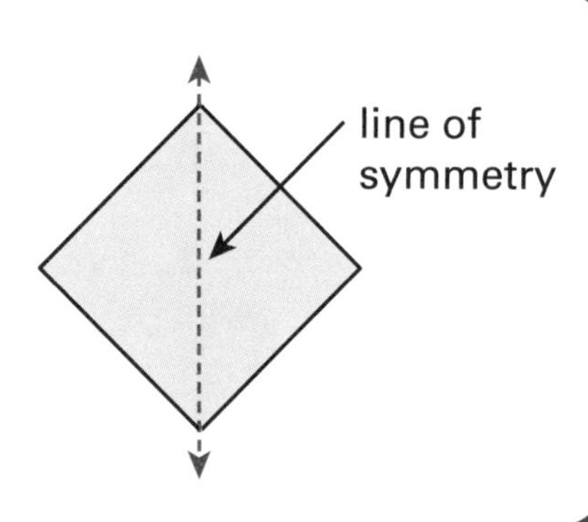

Let's Talk

Think of other ways to fold the figure so that the two parts match exactly. How many lines of symmetry does the figure have?

Fill in the blanks. Solve the problem.

The figure below is a school crossing sign.

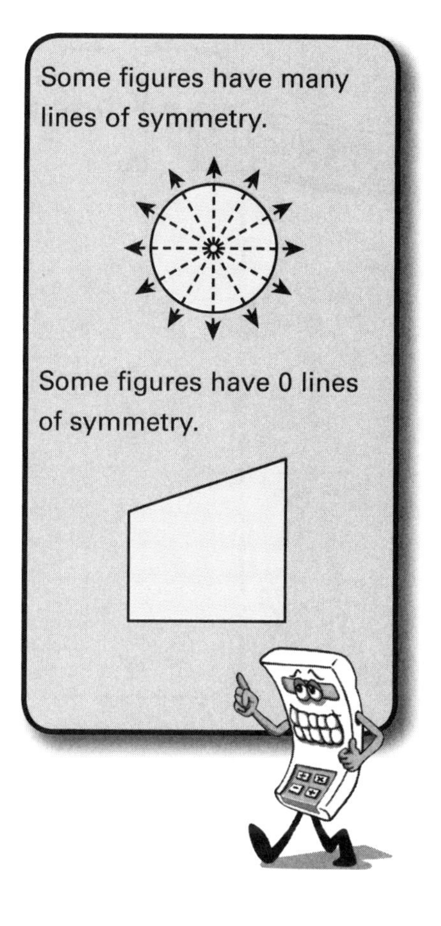

Does the figure have line symmetry?

- Look at the figure closely.

  Is there a way that you can fold it so that the two parts match exactly? _______

- If yes, draw the line of symmetry on the figure.

Solution: The figure _______________ line symmetry.

Your Turn **Now, use what you know to solve this problem.**

2. This figure has line symmetry. Draw a line of symmetry. Look for other lines of symmetry you can draw.

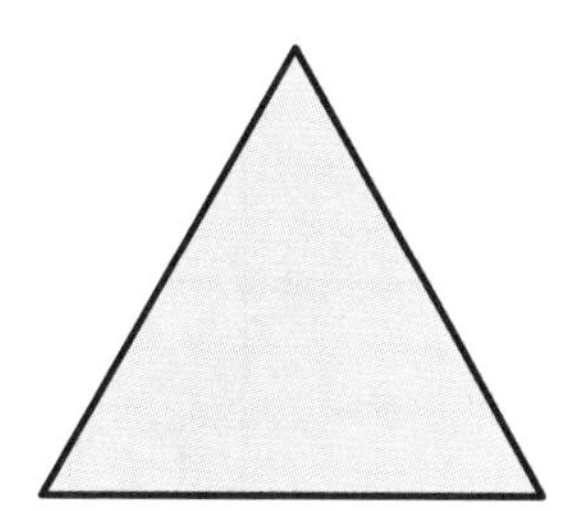

PART THREE: Choose the Right Answer

Solve the problem. Then read why each answer choice is correct or not correct.

Solve

Which pair of figures is congruent?

Ⓐ
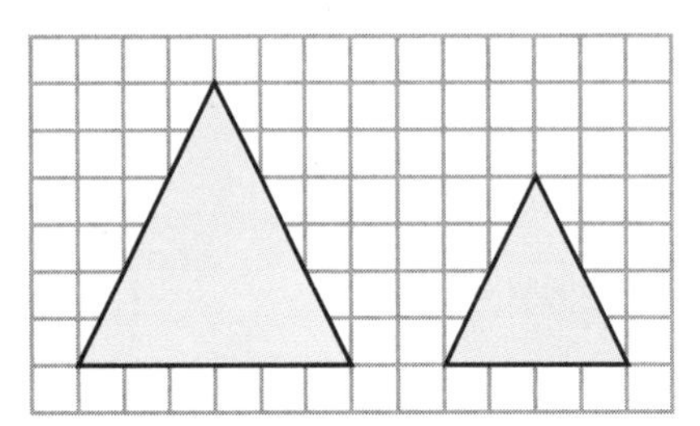

Ⓒ
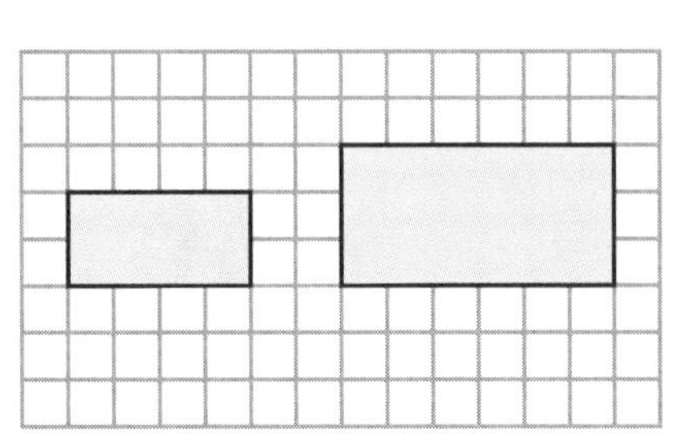

Ⓑ
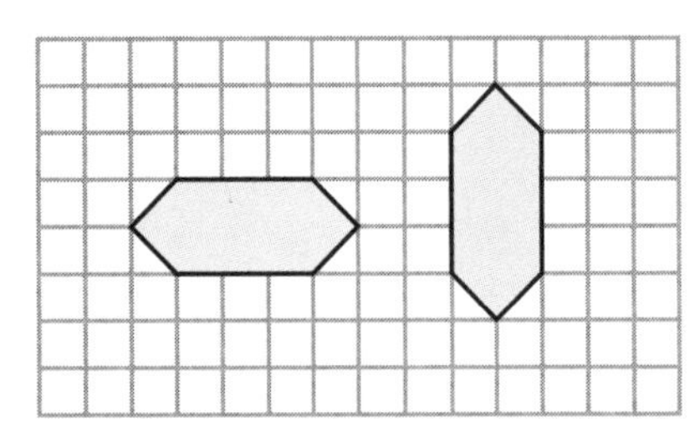

Ⓓ
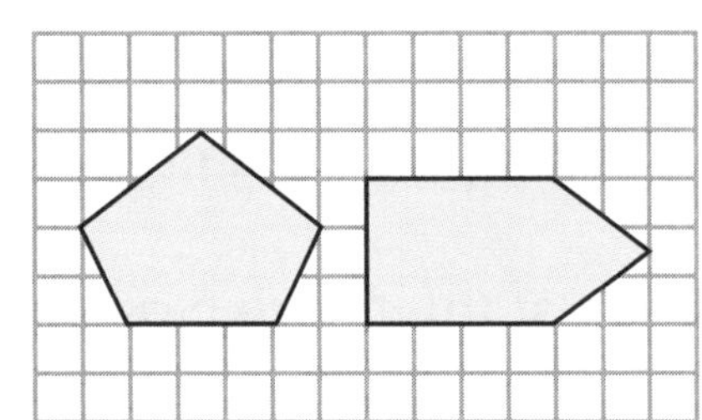

Check

Check to see if you chose the correct answer.

Congruent figures have the same shape and same size.
Only the two 6-sided figures have the same shape and size.

So, the correct answer is Ⓑ.

Why are the other answer choices not correct?

Ⓐ	These figures are the same shape but different sizes.
Ⓒ	These figures are the same shape but different sizes.
Ⓓ	These figures are not the same shape.

Your Turn **Solve each problem. Use the hints to avoid mistakes.**

- First, decide if the figures are the same shape. Then figure out if they are the same size.
- Think about whether one figure can be placed over the other and match exactly.
- Ask yourself if the figure can be folded in such a way that the parts match exactly.

3. José drew this figure.

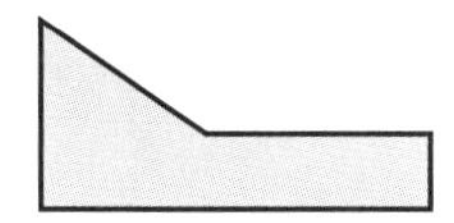

Which figure is congruent to José's figure?

Ⓐ 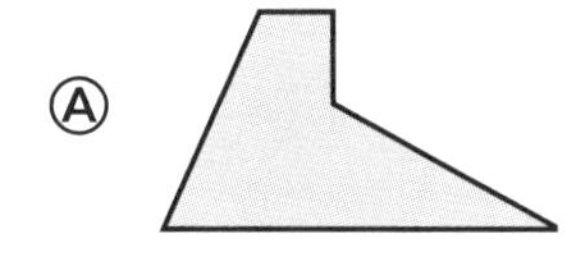

Ⓒ 

Ⓑ 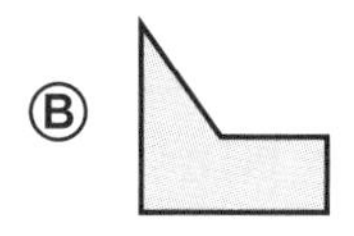

Ⓓ 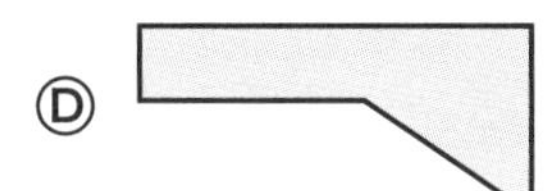

4. Which figures are congruent?

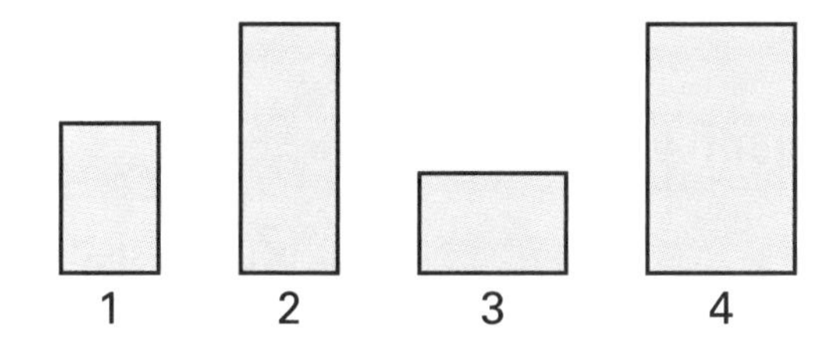

Ⓐ 1 and 2

Ⓑ 1 and 3

Ⓒ 2 and 4

Ⓓ 1, 2, and 3

5. Tyler made this sign for his room.

Which letters on the sign have line symmetry?

Ⓐ T and Y

Ⓑ T, Y, and E

Ⓒ T, Y, L, and E

Ⓓ T, Y, L, E, and R

6. How many lines of symmetry does this figure have?

Ⓐ 0

Ⓑ 1

Ⓒ 2

Ⓓ 3

Study the model. It is a good example of a written answer.

Student Model

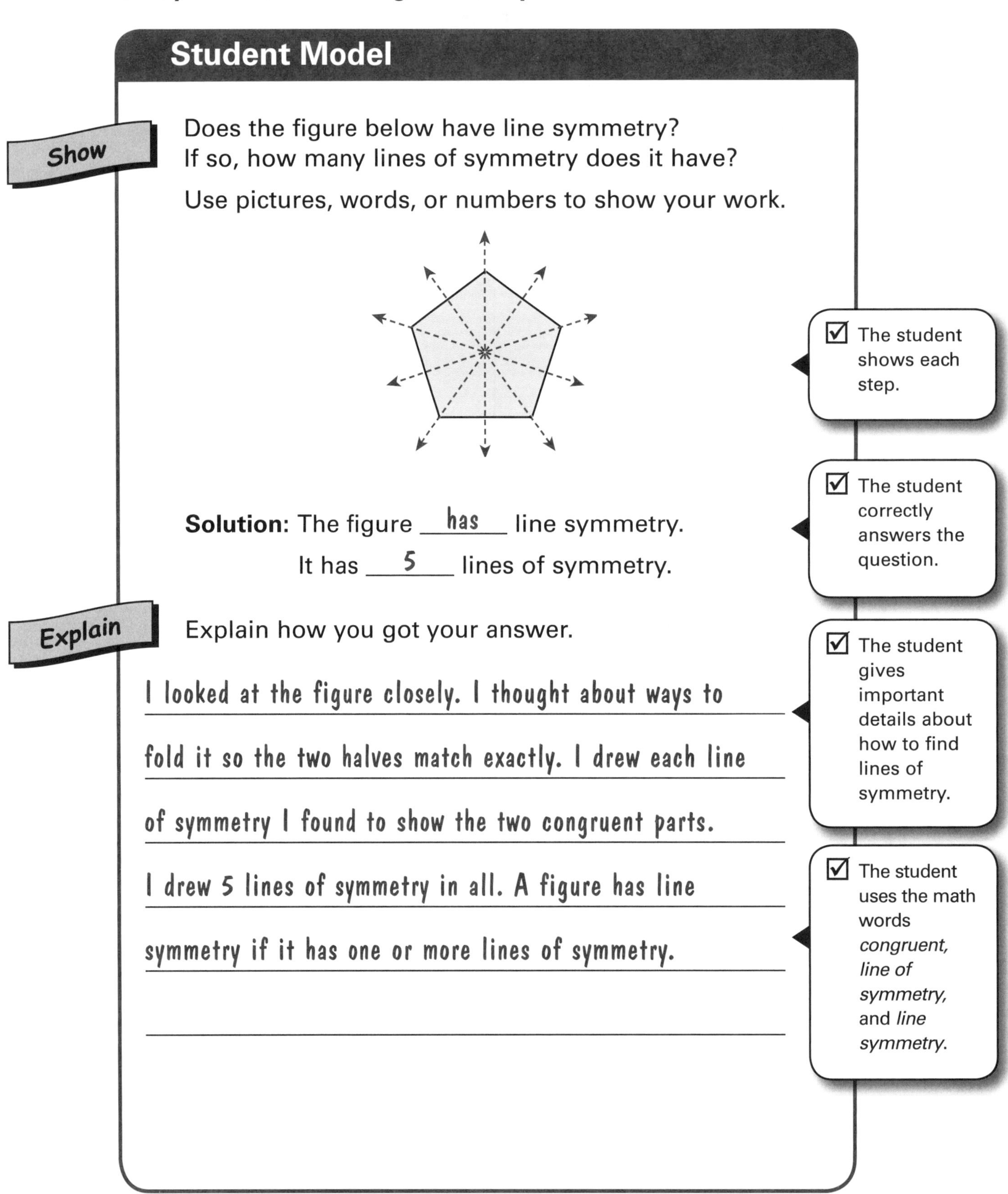

Your Turn **Solve the problem. Use what you learned from the model.**

CHECKLIST

Did you . . .

- ☐ show each step?
- ☐ answer the question asked?
- ☐ give important details?
- ☐ use math words?

7. Randy made the figure below in art class. Does Randy's figure have line symmetry? If so, how many lines of symmetry does his figure have?

Use pictures, words, or numbers to show your work.

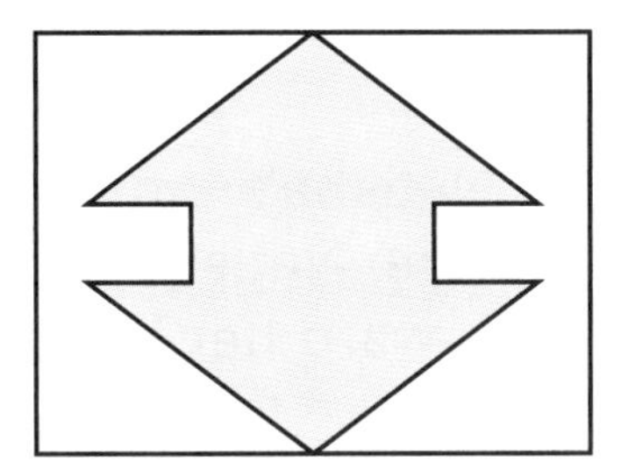

Solution: The figure ____________ line symmetry.

It has _______ lines of symmetry.

Explain how you got your answer.

____

____

____

____

____

As you solve congruence and symmetry problems, you may want to
- measure figures to check if they are the same size.
- picture in your mind ways to fold the figure so the two parts match. Each fold is a line of symmetry.

Solve each problem.

8. Which figures are congruent?

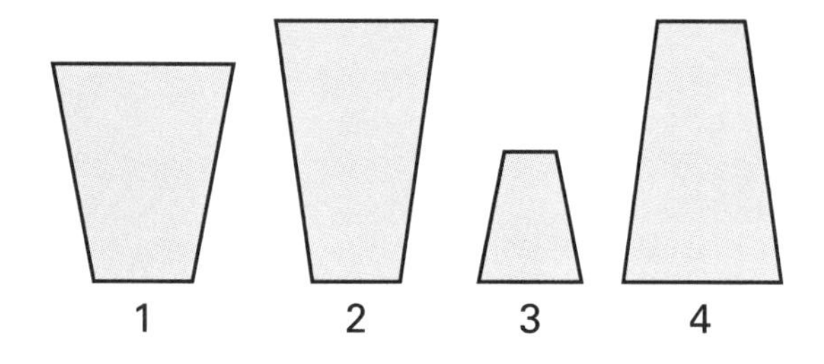

Ⓐ 2 and 4

Ⓑ 3 and 4

Ⓒ 2, 3, and 4

Ⓓ 1, 2, 3, and 4

9. Which pair of figures is congruent?

Ⓐ

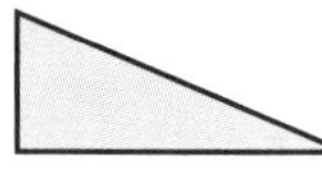

Ⓒ

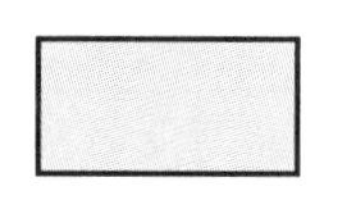

Ⓑ

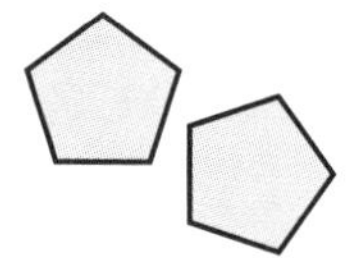

Ⓓ

10. Natisha's family is having a garage sale. Natisha drew an arrow to point toward her house.

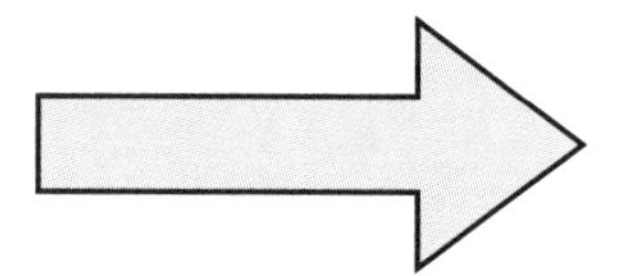

How many lines of symmetry does the arrow have?

Ⓐ 0

Ⓑ 1

Ⓒ 2

Ⓓ 7

11. Which shows a line of symmetry?

Ⓐ

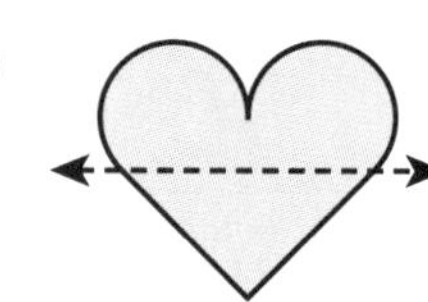

Ⓒ

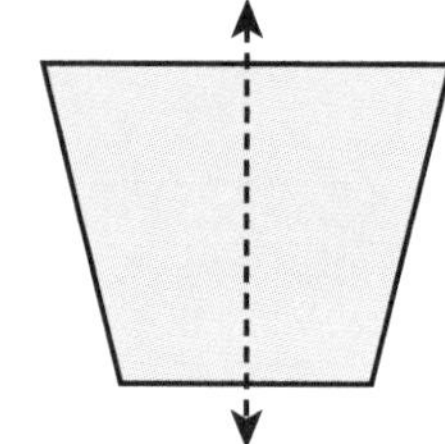

Ⓑ

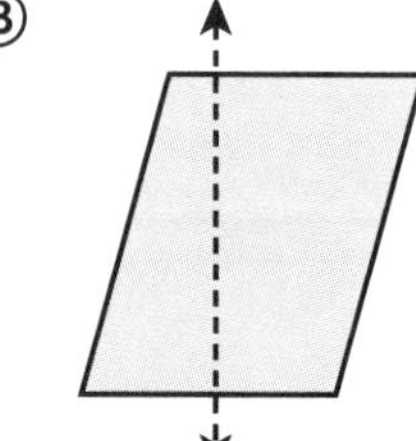

Ⓓ

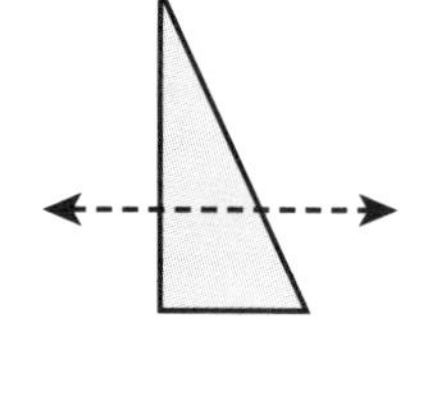

12. Which figure is congruent to Figure Y?

Y

Ⓐ Ⓒ

Ⓑ Ⓓ

13. Which letter does **not** have a line of symmetry?

Ⓐ M

Ⓑ S

Ⓒ T

Ⓓ O

14. Eric and Louann drew these figures on grid paper.

Eric's Figure

Louann's Figure

Are the figures congruent? ________

How do you know?

The figures ______________________

______________________________.

15. Gerrardo made a card for his friend.
He drew a figure on the front of the card.
How many lines of symmetry does the figure have?

Use pictures, words, or numbers to show your work.

Solution: The figure has ______ lines of symmetry.

Explain how you found your answer.

____

____

____

____

Lesson 14 LENGTH

PART ONE: Learn About Measuring to the Nearest $\frac{1}{2}$ Inch

How can you measure length to the nearest $\frac{1}{2}$ inch?

Explore

Length is the distance from one point to another point.

You can measure the lengths of objects in **inches**.

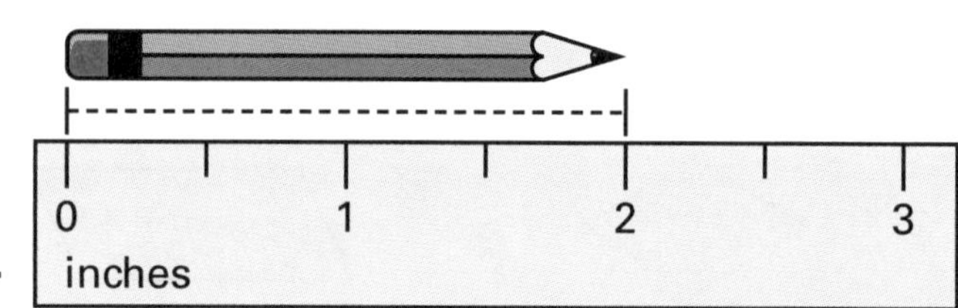

This pencil is 2 inches long.

How do you measure an object if its length is between whole inches?

Think

A ruler is like a **number line**.

The long marks with numbers show whole inches.

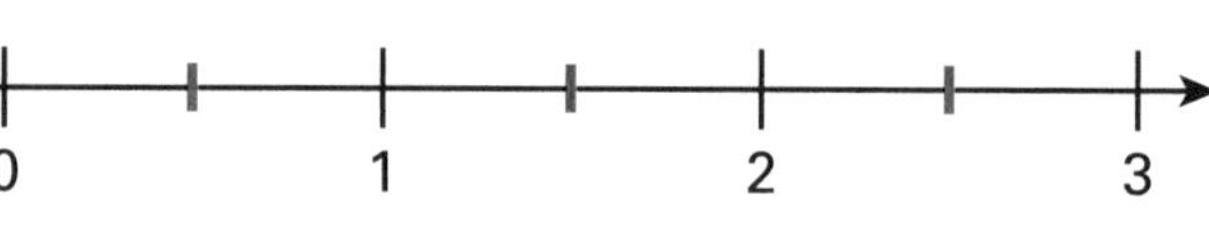

The shorter marks between the numbers show parts of an inch.

How many parts is each inch divided into? __2__ parts

What does each shorter mark stand for? __$\frac{1}{2}$__ inch

Connect

You can use a ruler to measure objects to the nearest $\frac{1}{2}$ inch.

The right edge of the ribbon lines up with the $2\frac{1}{2}$ mark on the ruler.

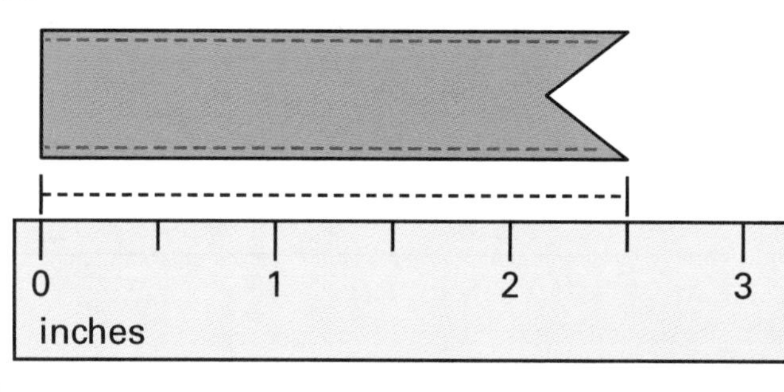

The ribbon is $2\frac{1}{2}$ inches long.

Let's Talk

One student measured the ribbon and said it was $1\frac{1}{2}$ inches long. What might that student have done wrong when measuring the ribbon's length?

Fill in the blanks. Solve the problem.

Marvin is eating a bread stick. What is the length of the bread stick to the nearest $\frac{1}{2}$ inch?

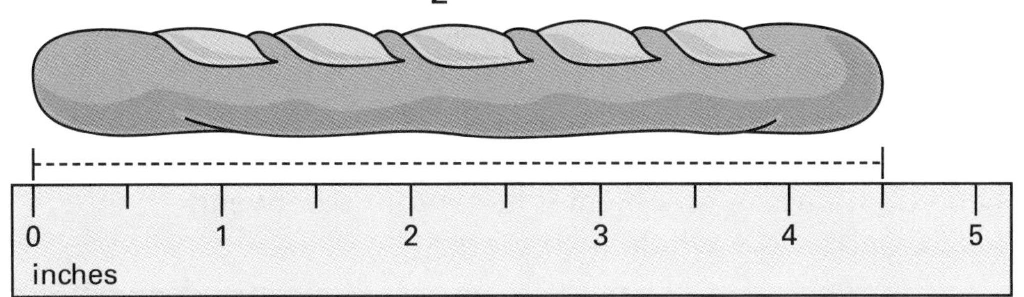

- Look at the ruler.

  The long marks with numbers show ________ inches.

  The short marks show _____ inches.

- The left edge of the bread stick lines up with _____ inches.

  The right edge of the bread stick lines up with _____ inches.

Solution: The bread stick is _____ inches long.

When you measure to the nearest $\frac{1}{2}$ inch, the length will either be

- a whole number, like 1, 2, or 3,

or

- a **fraction** or a **mixed number** with $\frac{1}{2}$, like $\frac{1}{2}$, $1\frac{1}{2}$, or $2\frac{1}{2}$.

Your Turn **Now, use what you know to solve this problem.**

1. What is the length of the fork to the nearest $\frac{1}{2}$ inch? Use a ruler to measure.

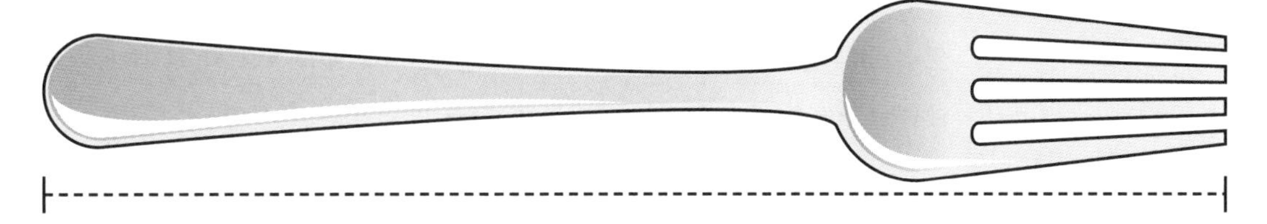

Ⓐ 4 inches

Ⓑ $4\frac{1}{2}$ inches

Ⓒ 5 inches

Ⓓ $5\frac{1}{2}$ inches

How can you measure length to the nearest $\frac{1}{4}$ inch?

Explore

You can use a ruler to measure objects to the nearest $\frac{1}{2}$ inch.

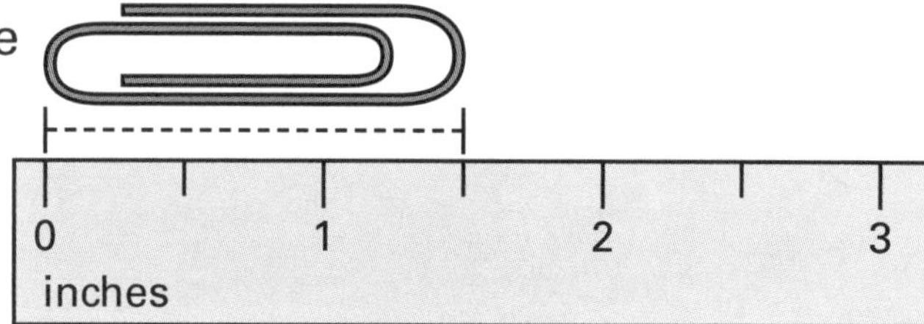

This paper clip is $1\frac{1}{2}$ inches long.

How can you measure an object if its length is between a half-inch mark and a whole-inch mark?

Think

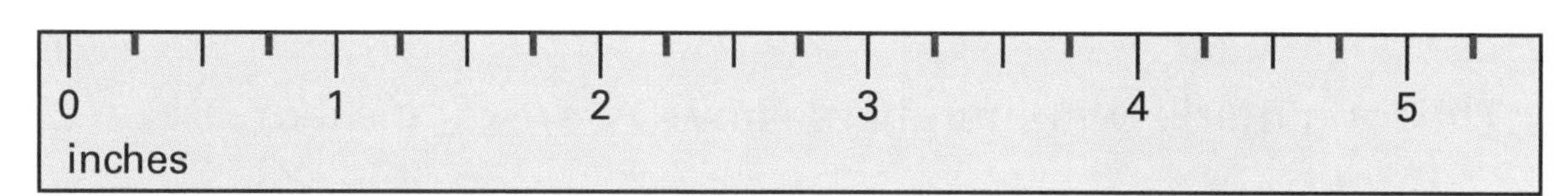

On this ruler, how many parts is each inch divided into? 4

What does each red mark stand for? $\frac{1}{4}$ inch

Connect

You can use a ruler to measure objects to the nearest $\frac{1}{4}$ inch.

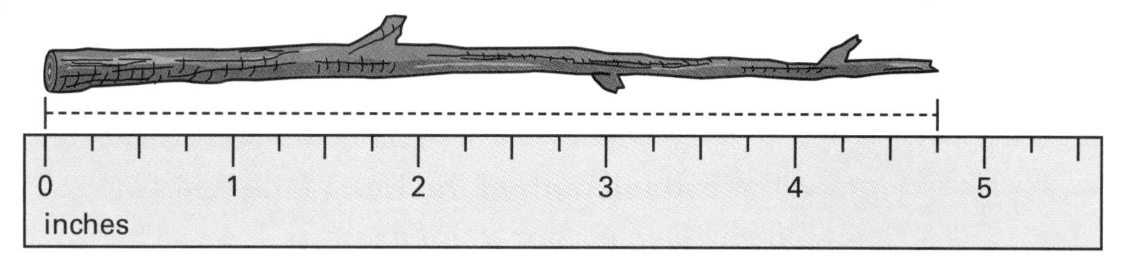

The right edge of the twig lines up with the $4\frac{3}{4}$ mark on the ruler. The twig is $4\frac{3}{4}$ inches long.

Let's Talk

The ribbon on page 134 is $2\frac{1}{2}$ inches long. Use a ruler to measure the ribbon to the nearest $\frac{1}{4}$ inch. What do you discover?

Fill in the blanks. Solve the problem.

Adriana is playing with a toy race car. What is the length of the race car to the nearest $\frac{1}{4}$ inch?

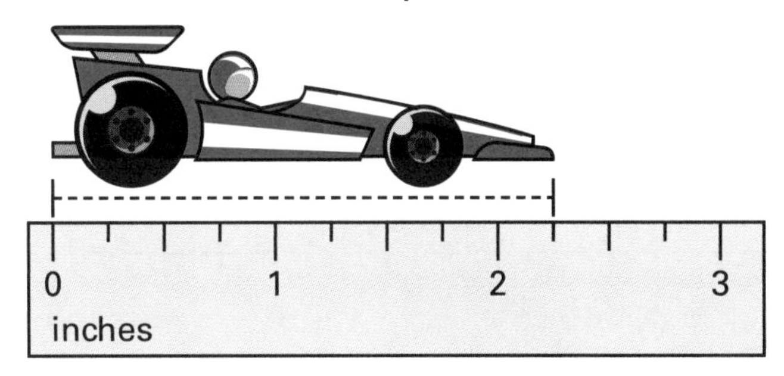

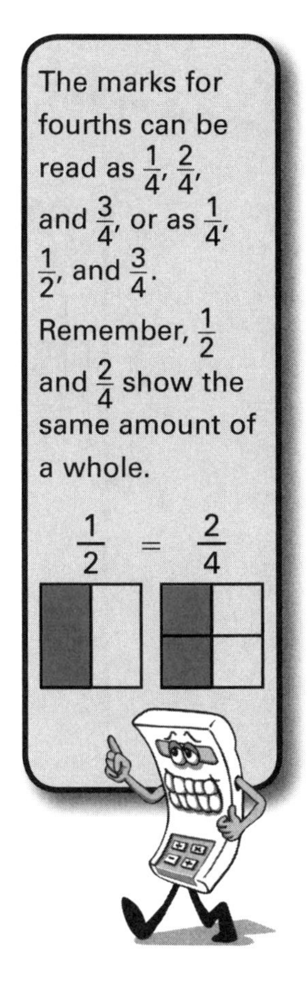

- Look at the ruler.

  The longest marks on the ruler show ________ inches.

  The next longest marks on the ruler show ____ inches.

  The shortest marks on the ruler show ____ inches.

- The left edge of the car lines up with ____ inches.

  The right edge of the car lines up with ____ inches.

Solution: The car is ____ inches long.

Your Turn **Now, use what you know to solve this problem.**

2. What is the length of the pen to the nearest $\frac{1}{4}$ inch? Use a ruler to measure.

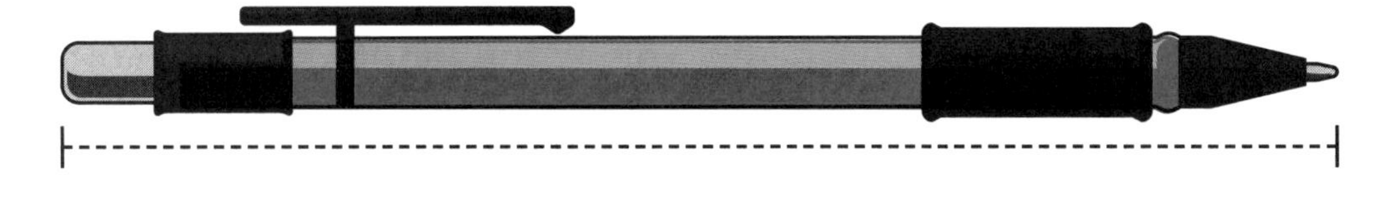

____ inches

Solve the problem. Then read why each answer choice is correct or not correct.

Solve

Nick got a new eraser. What is the length of the eraser to the nearest $\frac{1}{4}$ inch?

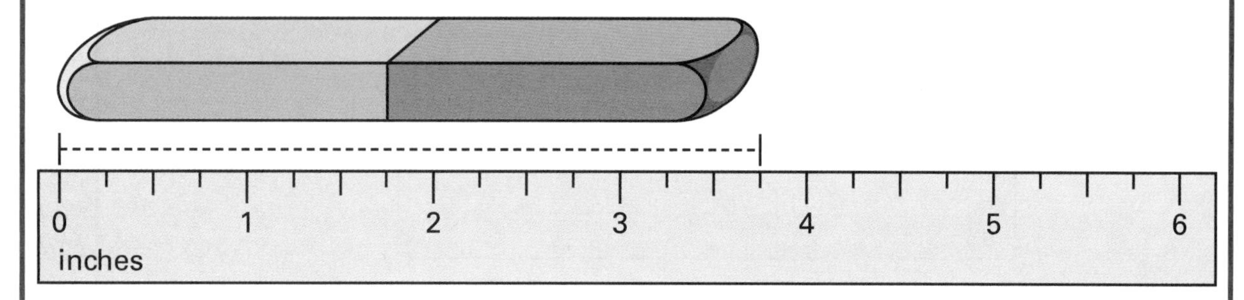

Ⓐ $3\frac{1}{4}$ inches

Ⓑ $3\frac{3}{4}$ inches

Ⓒ 4 inches

Ⓓ $4\frac{1}{4}$ inches

Check

Check to see if you chose the correct answer.

The left edge of the eraser lines up with zero on the ruler.

The right edge lines up with the mark for $3\frac{3}{4}$ inches.

So, the correct answer is Ⓑ.

Why are the other answer choices not correct?

Ⓐ $3\frac{1}{4}$ inches	This is the length shown by the first mark after the 3-inch mark. The eraser is longer than this.
Ⓒ 4 inches	This is the length shown by the long mark above the 4. The eraser is shorter than this.
Ⓓ $4\frac{1}{4}$ inches	This is the length shown by the first mark after the 4-inch mark. The eraser is shorter than this.

Your Turn **Solve each problem. Use the hints to avoid mistakes.**

- Make sure the left edge of the object to measure lines up with zero on the ruler.
- Carefully look at the ruler to find what mark lines up with the object's right edge.

3. Use a ruler to measure the stapler to the nearest $\frac{1}{2}$ inch.

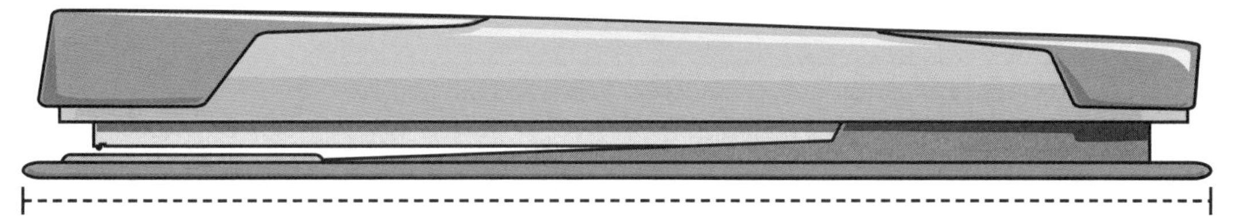

Ⓐ $4\frac{1}{2}$ inches Ⓑ 5 inches Ⓒ $5\frac{1}{2}$ inches Ⓓ 6 inches

4. Use a ruler to measure the leaf to the nearest $\frac{1}{4}$ inch.

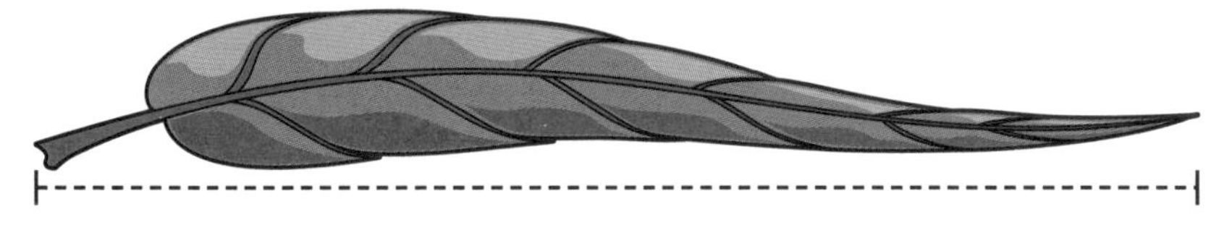

Ⓐ 4 inches Ⓑ $4\frac{1}{4}$ inches Ⓒ $4\frac{2}{4}$ inches Ⓓ $5\frac{1}{4}$ inches

5. Use a ruler to measure the book to the nearest $\frac{1}{2}$ inch.

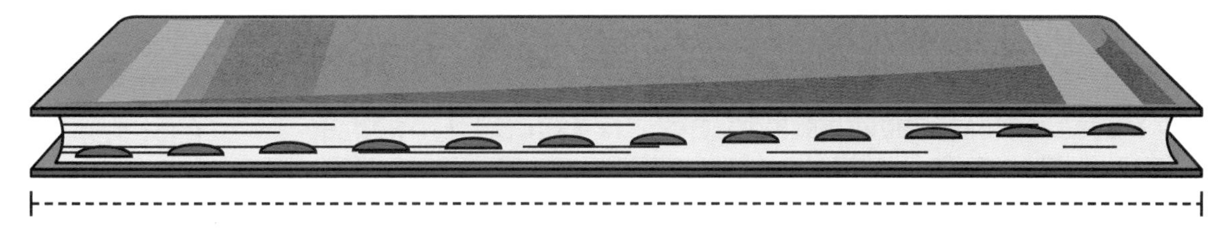

Ⓐ 5 inches Ⓑ $5\frac{1}{4}$ inches Ⓒ $5\frac{1}{2}$ inches Ⓓ 6 inches

6. Use a ruler to measure the cell phone to the nearest $\frac{1}{4}$ inch.

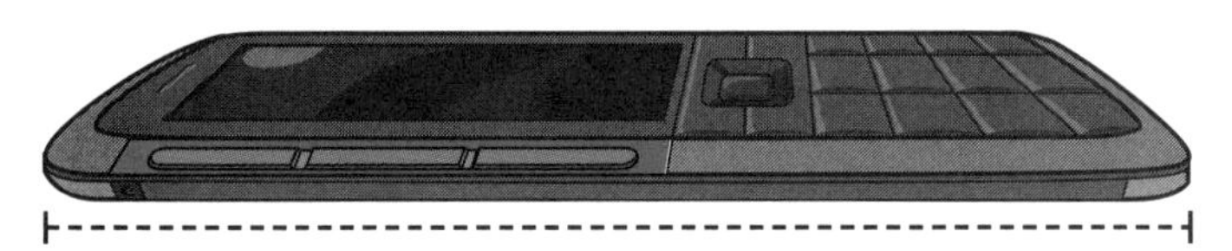

Ⓐ 3 inches Ⓑ $3\frac{1}{4}$ inches Ⓒ $3\frac{2}{4}$ inches Ⓓ $3\frac{3}{4}$ inches

Study the model. It is a good example of a written answer.

Student Model

Show

Marcel bought a new bookmark. He chose one that is $3\frac{3}{4}$ inches long. Which bookmark did he choose?

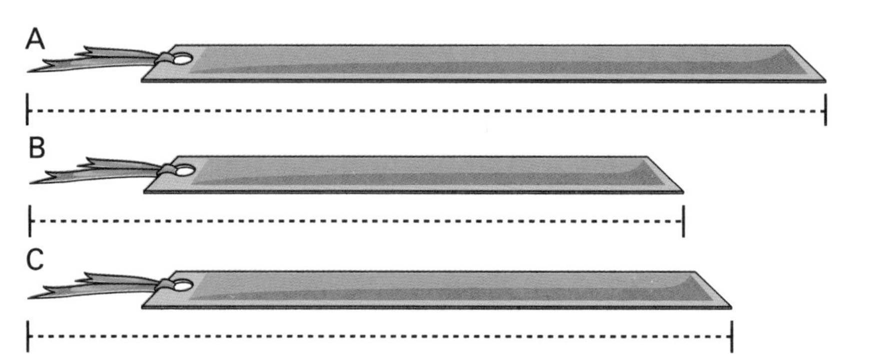

Use pictures, words, or numbers to show your work.

A: $4\frac{1}{4}$ inches B: $3\frac{2}{4}$ inches C: $3\frac{3}{4}$ inches

☑ The student shows each step.

Solution: Marcel chose bookmark C.

☑ The student correctly answers the question asked.

Explain

Explain how you got your answer.

I measured each bookmark to find its length. I lined up the zero on a ruler with the left edge of the bookmark. Then I looked at the right edge of the bookmark to see what it lined up with on the ruler. Bookmark C lined up with $3\frac{3}{4}$ inches, so Marcel chose bookmark C.

☑ The student gives important details about how to find the answer.

☑ The student uses the math words *measure, length, ruler,* and *inches.*

Your Turn **Solve the problem. Use what you learned from the model.**

7. Ron's pet fish is $2\frac{1}{4}$ inches long. Which fish is Ron's?

A

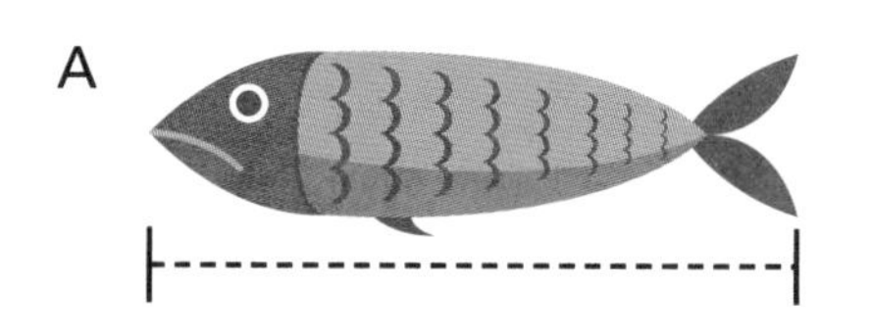

B

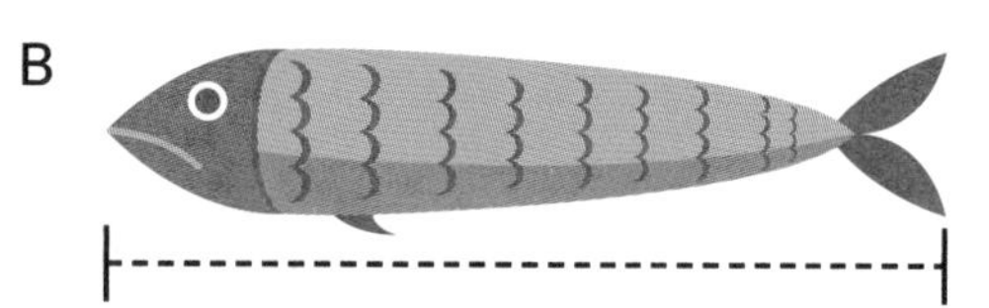

C

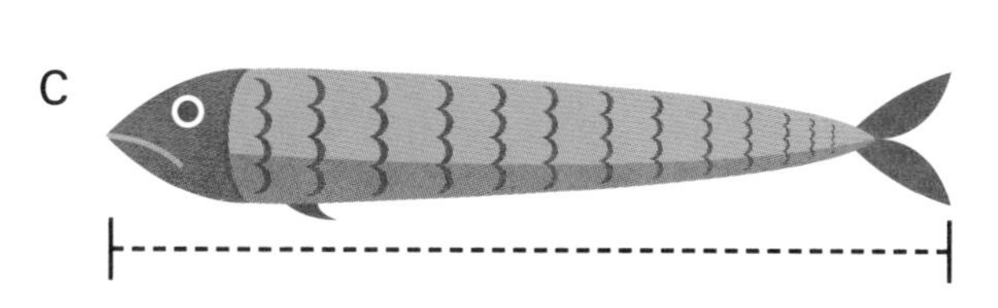

CHECKLIST

Did you . . .

- ☐ show each step?
- ☐ answer the question asked?
- ☐ give important details?
- ☐ use math words?

Use pictures, words, or numbers to show your work.

Solution: Ron's fish is fish _______.

Explain how you got your answer.

____

____

____

____

____

As you solve length problems, you should

- make sure your answer is a whole number, fraction, or mixed number with $\frac{1}{2}$ when you measure to the nearest $\frac{1}{2}$ inch.
- make sure your answer is a whole number, fraction, or mixed number with fourths when you measure to the nearest $\frac{1}{4}$ inch.
- measure each object twice to check your work.

Solve each problem.

Use the spoon for problems 8 and 9.

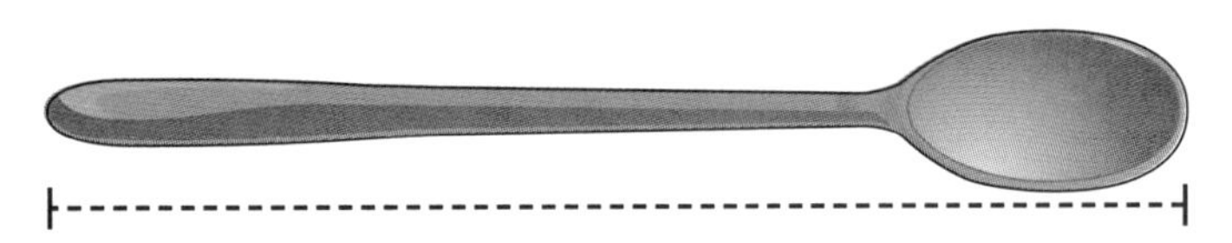

8. What is the length of the spoon to the nearest $\frac{1}{2}$ inch?

Ⓐ $3\frac{1}{2}$ inches Ⓑ 4 inches Ⓒ $4\frac{1}{2}$ inches Ⓓ 5 inches

9. How long is the spoon, measured to the nearest $\frac{1}{4}$ inch?

Ⓐ $3\frac{1}{4}$ inches Ⓑ $3\frac{2}{4}$ inches Ⓒ $3\frac{3}{4}$ inches Ⓓ $4\frac{2}{4}$ inches

10. What is the length of the watch to the nearest $\frac{1}{2}$ inch?

Ⓐ $4\frac{1}{2}$ inches Ⓑ 5 inches Ⓒ $5\frac{1}{2}$ inches Ⓓ 6 inches

11. What is the length of the carrot to the nearest $\frac{1}{4}$ inch?

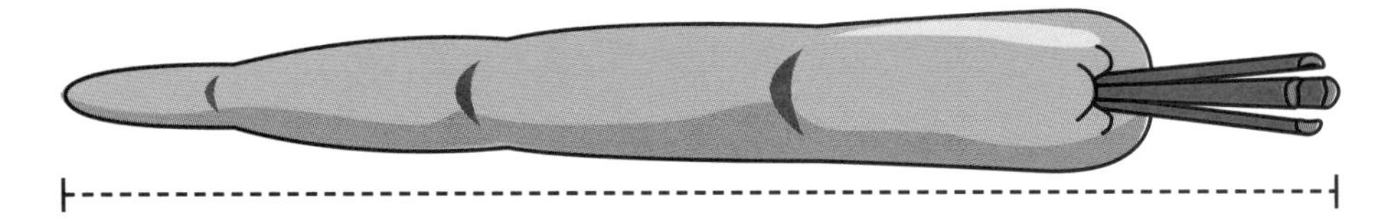

Ⓐ $3\frac{3}{4}$ inches Ⓑ $4\frac{1}{4}$ inches Ⓒ $4\frac{2}{4}$ inches Ⓓ $4\frac{3}{4}$ inches

Use the pictures for problems 12 and 13.

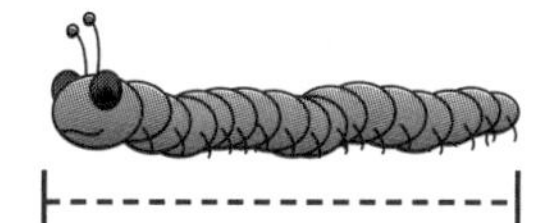

12. How long is the ant?

Ⓐ $\frac{3}{4}$ inch

Ⓑ 1 inch

Ⓒ $1\frac{1}{4}$ inches

Ⓓ $1\frac{2}{4}$ inches

13. How long is the caterpillar?

Ⓐ $\frac{3}{4}$ inch

Ⓑ 1 inch

Ⓒ $1\frac{1}{4}$ inches

Ⓓ $1\frac{2}{4}$ inches

14. Monique is eating a celery stick.

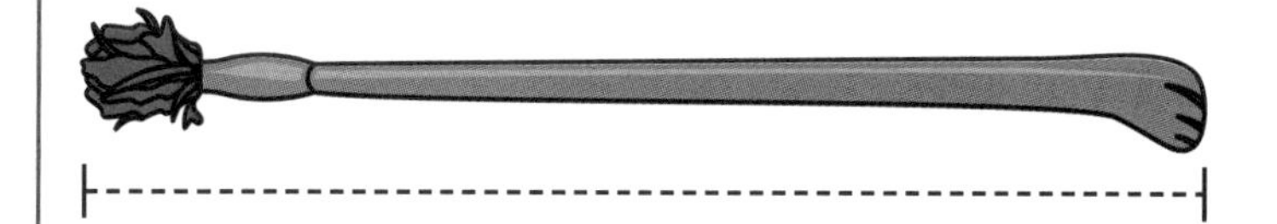

How long is the celery stick, measured to the nearest $\frac{1}{2}$ inch?

_______ inches

How long is the celery stick, measured to the nearest $\frac{1}{4}$ inch?

_______ inches

15. Rita, Hector, and Jonah drew straws to decide what movie to see. The person with the longest straw got to choose the movie. Who chose the movie? Measure the length of each straw to find out.

Rita's Straw

Hector's Straw

Jonah's Straw

Use pictures, words, or numbers to show your work.

Solution: _______________ chose the movie.

Explain how you got your answer.

____

____

____

Lesson 15 PERIMETER

PART ONE: Learn About Using Addition to Find Perimeter

How can you find the perimeter of any polygon?

Explore

A **polygon** is a closed figure with 3 or more straight sides.

Polygons

Not Polygons

How can you find the distance around a polygon?

Think

Perimeter is the distance around a polygon.

How many sides does this polygon have? 6

How many centimeters long is each side?

4 cm, 2 cm, 5 cm, 2 cm, 3 cm, 1 cm

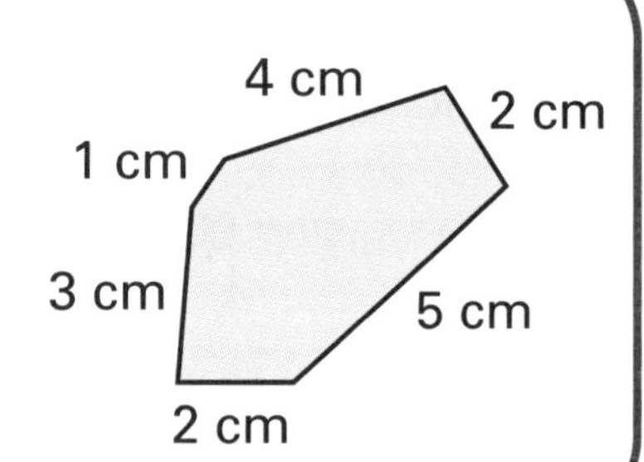

Connect

To find the perimeter of a polygon, you can add the lengths of all its sides.

Perimeter $= 4 + 2 + 5 + 2 + 3 + 1 = 17$

The perimeter of this polygon is 17 centimeters.

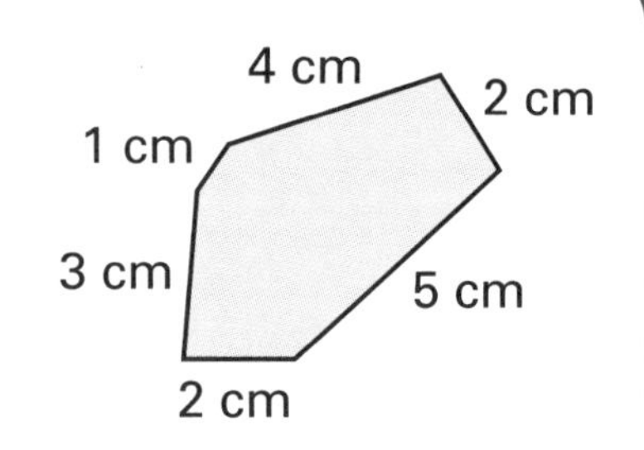

Let's Talk

Can you find the perimeter of this figure? Why or why not?

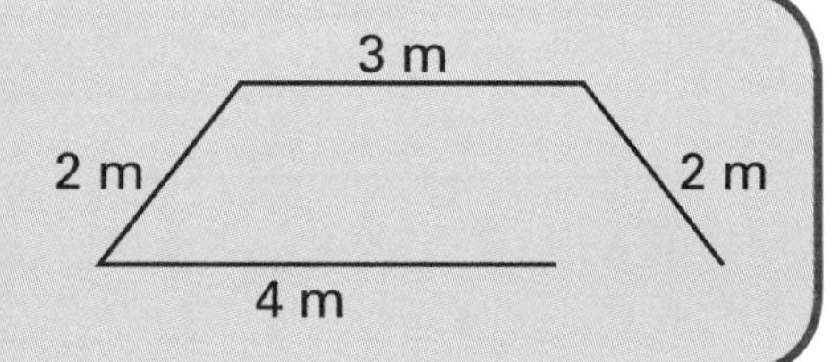

Fill in the blanks. Solve the problem.

What is the perimeter of the polygon?

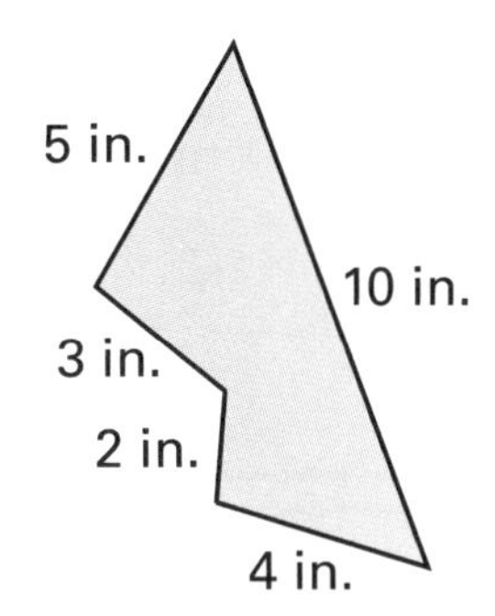

- How many sides does the polygon have? ____

  How many inches long is each side?

  ____ in., ____ in., ____ in., ____ in., ____ in.

- Add the lengths of the sides to find the perimeter.

  ____ + ____ + ____ + ____ + ____ = ____

Solution: The perimeter of the polygon is ____ inches.

Your Turn **Now, use what you know to solve this problem.**

1. What is the perimeter of the polygon?

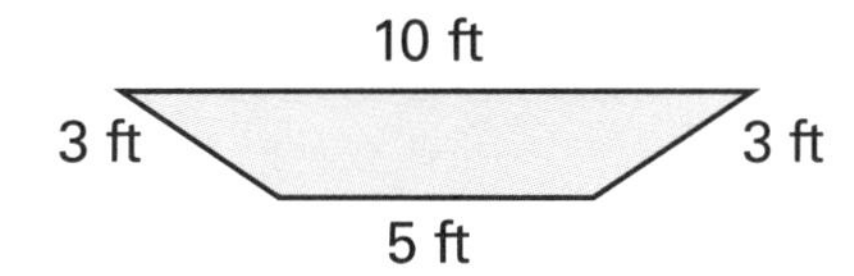

Ⓐ 16 feet

Ⓑ 18 feet

Ⓒ 21 feet

Ⓓ 26 feet

How can you find the perimeter of a rectangle?

Explore

You know one way to find the perimeter of a **rectangle**. You add the lengths of its sides.

Perimeter = 2 + 1 + 2 + 1 = 6 meters

What is another way to find the perimeter of a rectangle?

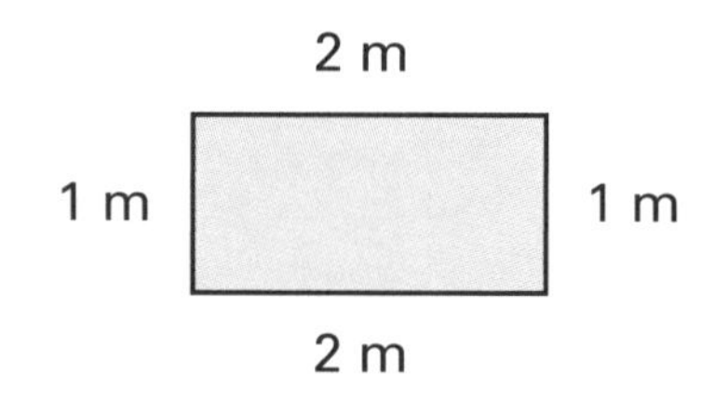

Think

Opposite sides of a rectangle always have the same measure.

The length of side *a* is 5 inches.

What is the length of side *c*? 5 inches

The width of side *b* is 4 inches.

What is the width of side *d*? 4 inches

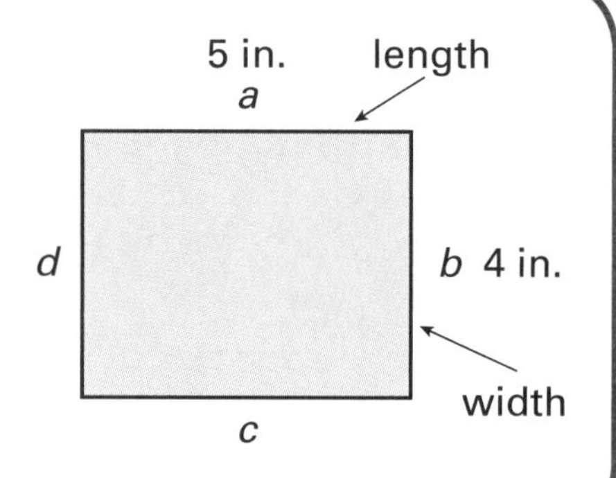

Connect

There are two ways to find the perimeter of a rectangle.

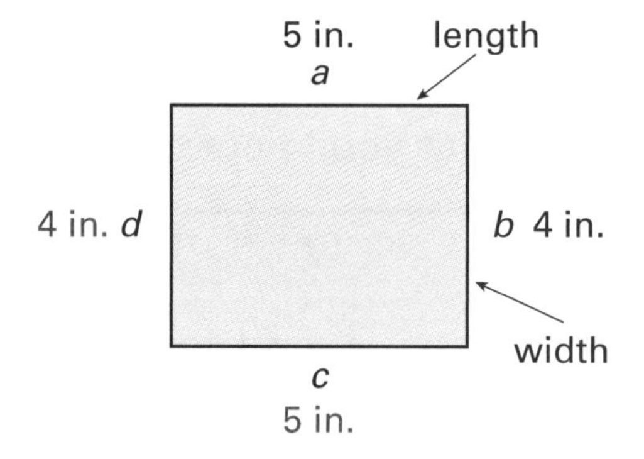

Add all four sides.	OR	Find twice the length.	$2 \times 5 = 10$
$5 + 4 + 5 + 4 = 18$		Find twice the width.	$2 \times 4 = 8$
		Then add.	$10 + 8 = 18$

The perimeter of the rectangle is 18 inches.

Let's Talk

A **square** is a rectangle that has four equal sides.
What is a quick way to find the perimeter of a square?

Fill in the blanks. Solve the problem.

What is the perimeter of the rectangle?

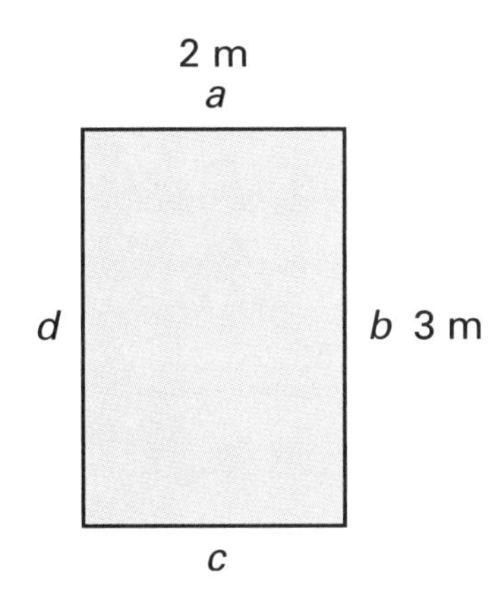

The length of a rectangle is the longer side. The shorter side is called the width.

- Find the measure of each pair of opposite sides.

  The length of side b is _____ meters.

  What is the length of side d? _____ meters

  The width of side a is _____ meters.

  What is the width of side c? _____ meters

- Find twice the length and twice the width.

  Length: $2 \times$ _____ = _____ Width: $2 \times$ _____ = _____

- Add the lengths and widths.

  _____ + _____ = _____

Solution: The perimeter of the rectangle is _____ meters.

Now, use what you know to solve this problem.

2. What is the perimeter of the rectangle?

_____ centimeters

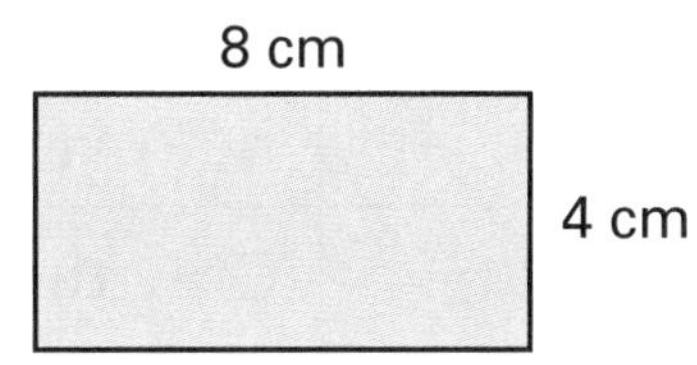

Solve the problem. Then read why each answer choice is correct or not correct.

Solve

Leah is buying fencing to build a pen for her dog. The pen has the shape of the rectangle shown.

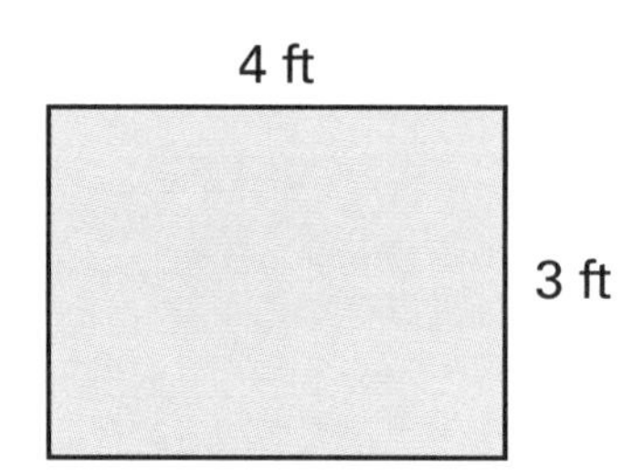

How much fencing should Leah buy?

Ⓐ 7 feet

Ⓑ 8 feet

Ⓒ 11 feet

Ⓓ 14 feet

Check

Check to see if you chose the correct answer.

Multiply the length by 2. $2 \times 4 = 8$

Multiply the width by 2. $2 \times 3 = 6$

Then add the lengths and widths. $8 + 6 = 14$

The perimeter is 14 feet.

So, the right answer is Ⓓ.

Why are the other answer choices not correct?

Ⓐ 7 feet	Only one length and one width were added, not twice the length and twice the width.
Ⓑ 8 feet	Only the two lengths were added.
Ⓒ 11 feet	One of the widths was not added.

Your Turn **Solve each problem. Use the hints to avoid mistakes.**

- Remember to add the lengths of all sides of the polygon.
- Be sure to add carefully, and then check your addition.

3. Which addition sentence shows how to find the perimeter of the polygon?

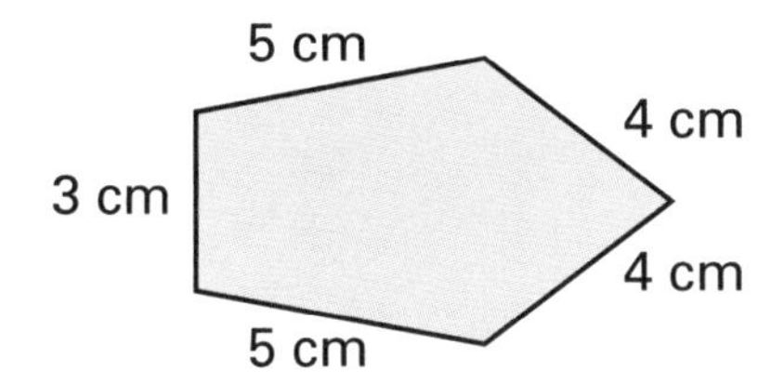

Ⓐ $3 + 5 + 4 = 12$

Ⓑ $3 + 5 + 4 + 4 + 3 = 19$

Ⓒ $3 + 5 + 4 + 4 + 5 = 21$

Ⓓ $3 + 5 + 4 + 4 + 5 + 3 = 24$

4. What is the perimeter of the square?

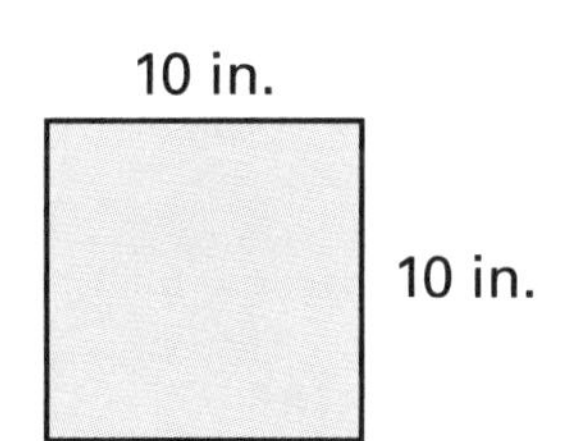

Ⓐ 10 inches

Ⓑ 20 inches

Ⓒ 30 inches

Ⓓ 40 inches

5. What is the perimeter of the triangle?

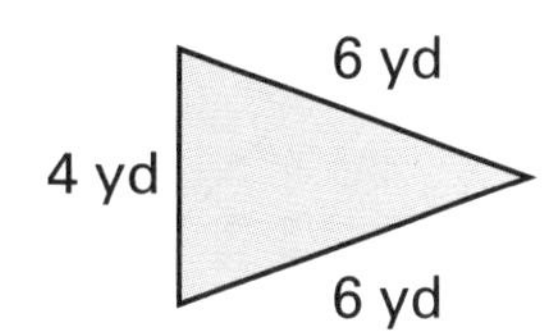

Ⓐ 10 yards

Ⓑ 16 yards

Ⓒ 18 yards

Ⓓ 20 yards

6. Michael plans to buy wood to make the picture frame below.

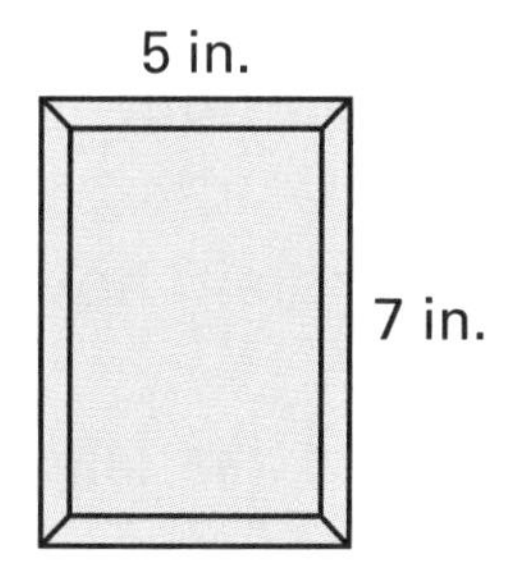

How much wood should he buy?

Ⓐ 12 inches

Ⓑ 17 inches

Ⓒ 21 inches

Ⓓ 24 inches

Study the model. It is a good example of a written answer.

Student Model

Show

A school wants to put a rubber curb around its playground. The playground has the shape shown.

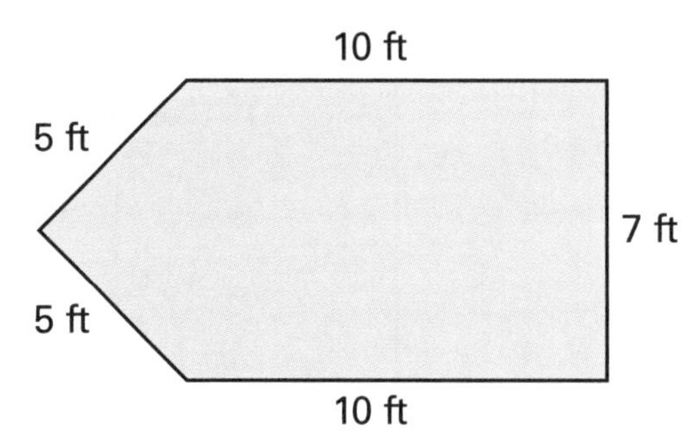

How many feet of rubber curb should the school buy?

Use pictures, words, or numbers to show your work.

Add lengths of 5 sides.

Perimeter $= 10 + 7 + 10 + 5 + 5$

Perimeter $= 37$ feet

Solution: 37 feet

Explain how you got your answer.

I added the lengths of all the sides to find the perimeter of the polygon. $10 + 7 + 10 + 5 + 5 = 37$

The school should buy 37 feet of rubber curb.

☑ The student shows each step.

☑ The student correctly answers the question asked.

☑ The student gives important details about how to find the perimeter.

☑ The student uses the math words *lengths*, *perimeter*, and *polygon*.

Your Turn **Solve the problem. Use what you learned from the model.**

7. Chantal wants to tape a poster to a wall in her room. The poster is in the shape of the rectangle shown.

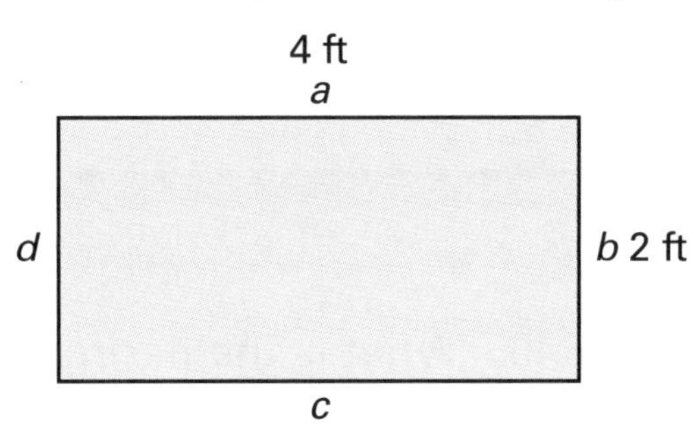

Chantal will put tape along the sides in back of the poster. How much tape will she need?

Use pictures, words, or numbers to show your work.

CHECKLIST

Did you . . .

- ☐ show each step?
- ☐ answer the question asked?
- ☐ give important details?
- ☐ use math words?

Solution: _____ feet

Explain how you got your answer.

____

____

____

____

____

____

As you solve perimeter problems, you may want to
- be sure the number of addends in your addition sentence is the same as the number of sides.
- check your multiplication when finding the perimeter of rectangles or squares.

Solve each problem.

8. Which addition sentence shows how to find the perimeter of the polygon?

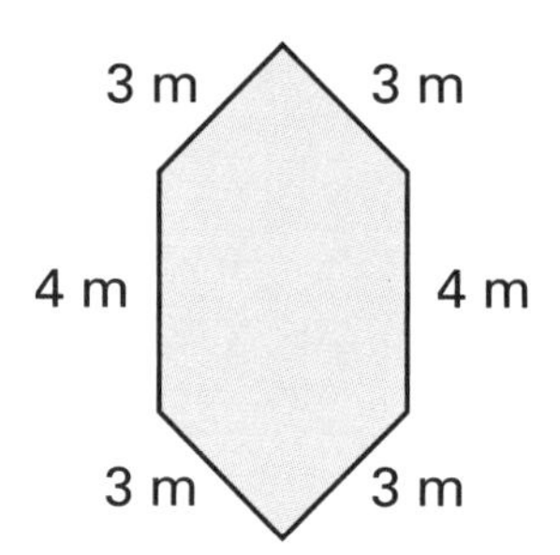

Ⓐ $3 + 4 + 3 + 3 + 4 = 17$

Ⓑ $3 + 4 + 3 + 3 + 4 + 3 = 20$

Ⓒ $3 + 4 + 3 + 3 + 4 + 4 = 21$

Ⓓ $3 + 4 + 3 + 3 + 4 + 3 + 4 = 24$

9. Carla and her friends were playing stickball. She used a piece of chalk to draw home plate on the pavement.

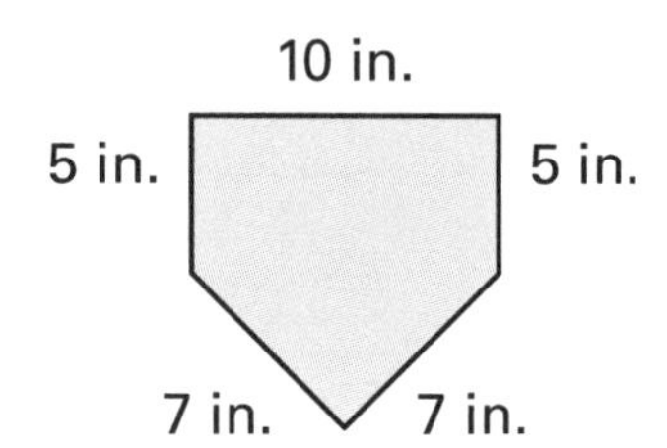

What is the perimeter of home plate?

Ⓐ 22 inches
Ⓑ 24 inches
Ⓒ 34 inches
Ⓓ 44 inches

10. What is the perimeter of the rectangle?

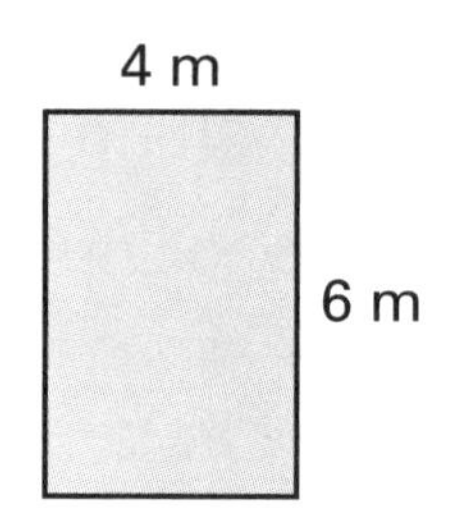

Ⓐ 10 meters

Ⓑ 12 meters

Ⓒ 16 meters

Ⓓ 20 meters

11. Justin went swimming in the pool shown below.

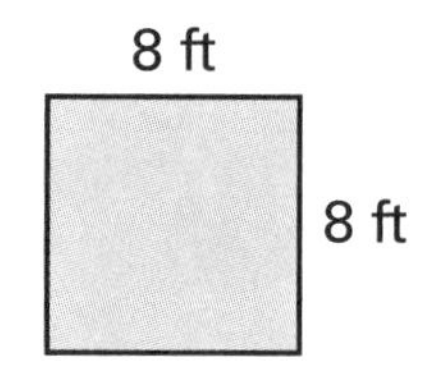

What is the distance around the pool?

Ⓐ 8 feet
Ⓑ 16 feet
Ⓒ 32 feet
Ⓓ 64 feet

12. In art class, Sean used yarn to create the triangular shape below.

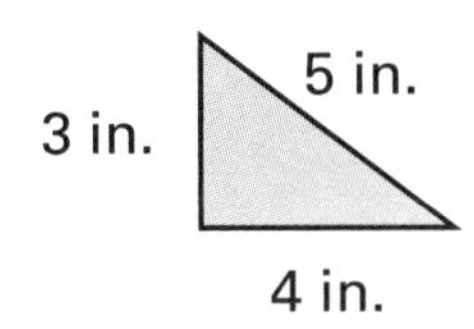

How many inches of yarn did he use?

Ⓐ 8 inches

Ⓑ 9 inches

Ⓒ 12 inches

Ⓓ 15 inches

13. What is the perimeter of the polygon?

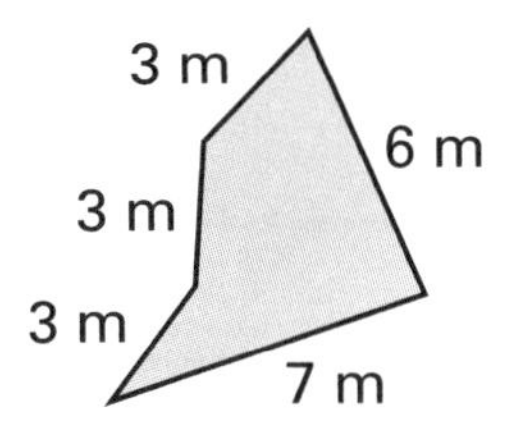

Ⓐ 19 meters

Ⓑ 21 meters

Ⓒ 22 meters

Ⓓ 25 meters

14. Mr. Brown's class made a collage out of pictures cut from magazines. Jenny cut a picture in the shape shown.

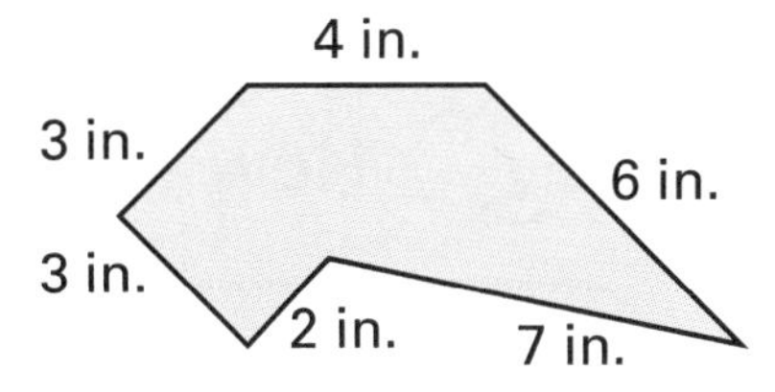

Write a number sentence to show how to find the perimeter of Jenny's picture.

____

15. Madison used wooden boards to build a border around her garden. What is the perimeter of her garden with its border?

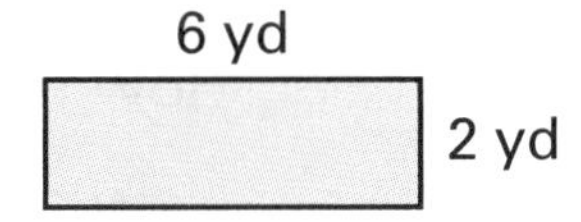

Use pictures, words, or numbers to show your work.

Solution: _____ yards

Explain how you found your answer.

____

____

____

____

Lesson 16 PICTOGRAPHS AND BAR GRAPHS

PART ONE: Learn About Pictographs

How can you use a pictograph to compare data?

Explore

A **table** is a way to show data.
Data are facts about people or things.

What is another way to show data so they are easy to compare?

Basketball Scores			
Name	Jane	Calvin	Ming
Points	15	10	20

Think

A **pictograph** shows data with pictures.
A **key** tells how many each picture stands for.

This pictograph shows how many points each player scored.

Each basketball stands for __5__ points.

How many basketballs are there for Jane? __3__

How many basketballs are there for Calvin? __2__

Basketball Scores	
Jane	🏀🏀🏀
Calvin	🏀🏀
Ming	🏀🏀🏀🏀
Key: 🏀 = 5 points	

Connect

Find how many more points Jane scored than Calvin.
First, find the number of points for each player.

Jane's score: $3 \times 5 = 15$ points
Calvin's score: $2 \times 5 = 10$ points

Then, subtract to compare. $15 - 10 = 5$ points
Jane scored 5 more points than Calvin.

Let's Talk

Suppose each ball stood for 3 points. How would the number of points for each player change?

Fill in the blanks. Solve the problem.

The students in Mr. Ito's class voted for their favorite season. The pictograph shows the data.

Favorite Season

Winter	🯅 🯅 🯅
Spring	🯅 🯅
Summer	🯅 🯅 🯅 🯅
Fall	🯅 🯅 🯅
Key: 🯅 = 2 votes	

The pictures in a pictograph can stand for 1 or a number greater than 1.

Which season got fewer votes, fall or summer? How many fewer votes did that season get?

- How many votes does each person stand for? ____

  How many people are there for fall? ____

  How many people are there for summer? ____

- Multiply to find the number of votes for each season.

  fall: ____ × ____ = ____ votes

  summer: ____ × ____ = ____ votes

- Subtract to compare the data for each season.

  ____ − ____ = ____ votes

Solution: __________ got ____ fewer votes than __________.

Your Turn **Now, use what you know to solve this problem.**

1. How many more votes did winter get than spring?

Ⓐ 1 Ⓑ 2 Ⓒ 3 Ⓓ 4

How can you use a bar graph to compare data?

Explore

There are many ways to show data.

How can you use bars to show data?

Students' Pets			
Pet	Rabbit	Dog	Cat
Number of Students	9	6	5

Think

A **bar graph** shows data with bars. A **scale** shows the number each bar stands for.

This bar graph shows the pets students have.

Look at the top of each bar. Read the number to the left.

How many students have a cat? 5

How many students have a rabbit? 9

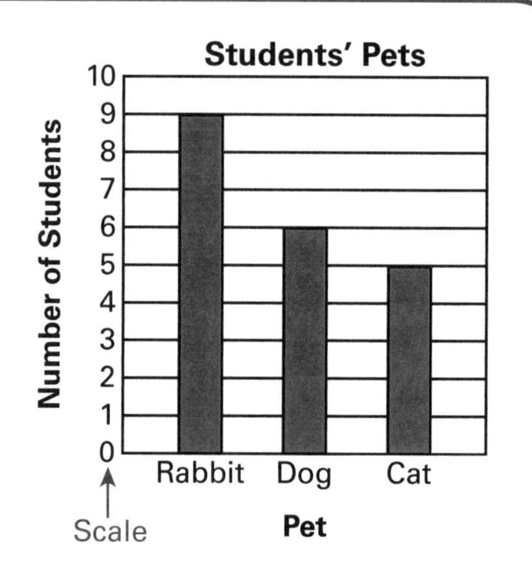

Connect

Find how many more students have rabbits than cats.

Subtract to compare.

$9 - 5 = 4$

4 more students have rabbits than cats.

Let's Talk

Suppose every student has one pet. How can you find the number of students in the class? Explain.

Fill in the blanks. Solve the problem.

The bar graph shows the number of books students checked out of the library.

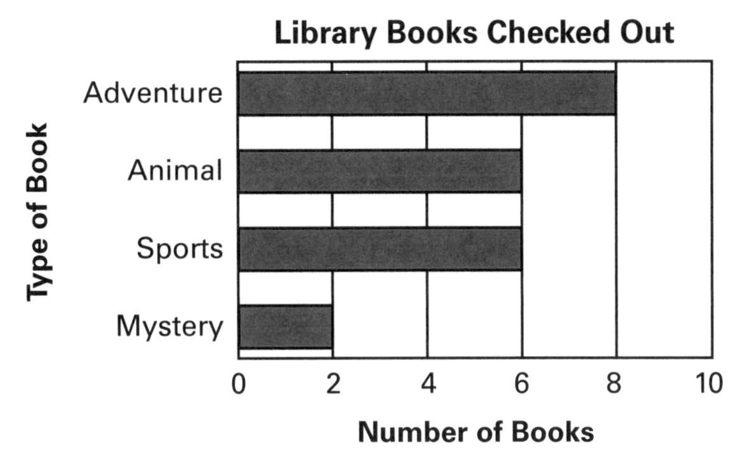

How many more animal books than mystery books did students check out?

■ Look at where the bar for animal books ends.

Read the number below the end of the bar.

How many animal books were checked out? _____

■ Look at where the bar for mystery books ends.

Read the number below the end of the bar.

How many mystery books were checked out? _____

■ Subtract to compare the data. _____ − _____ = _____ books

Solution: Students checked out _____ more animal books than mystery books.

Now, use what you know to solve this problem.

2. How many fewer sports books than adventure books did students check out?

_____ fewer sports books than adventure books

Solve the problem. Then read why each answer choice is correct or not correct.

Solve

The pictograph shows how many students ordered different kinds of lunches.

How many more students ordered pizza than tacos?

Ⓐ 4

Ⓑ 6

Ⓒ 12

Ⓓ 24

School Lunch Orders

Chicken	🍴🍴🍴🍴🍴
Salad	🍴🍴🍴🍴
Pizza	🍴🍴🍴🍴🍴🍴
Tacos	🍴🍴
Key: 🍴 = 3 students	

Check

Check to see if you chose the correct answer.

Each fork stands for 3 students.

There are 6 forks above pizza. $6 \times 3 = 18$

There are 2 forks above tacos. $2 \times 3 = 6$

$18 - 6 = 12$

So, the correct answer is Ⓒ.

Why are the other answer choices not correct?

Ⓐ 4	The values of the forks in each group should be subtracted, not the numbers of forks.
Ⓑ 6	Pizza and tacos should be compared, not pizza and salad.
Ⓓ 24	The values of the forks in each group should be subtracted, not added.

Your Turn **Solve each problem. Use the hints to avoid mistakes.**

- Count the pictures in a pictograph carefully.
- Use the key in a pictograph to find how many each picture stands for.
- On a bar graph, carefully follow the top or end of a bar to the number on the scale.

Use the pictograph for problems 3 and 4.

The pictograph shows how many puppets the students in an art class made.

Making Puppets

3. Who made 10 puppets?

   Ⓐ Rosa
   Ⓑ Jon
   Ⓒ Sherril
   Ⓓ Bill

4. How many more puppets did Rosa make than Bill?

   Ⓐ 1
   Ⓑ 2
   Ⓒ 5
   Ⓓ 6

Use the bar graph for problems 5 and 6.

The children in a summer camp voted on their favorite snacks. The bar graph shows the data.

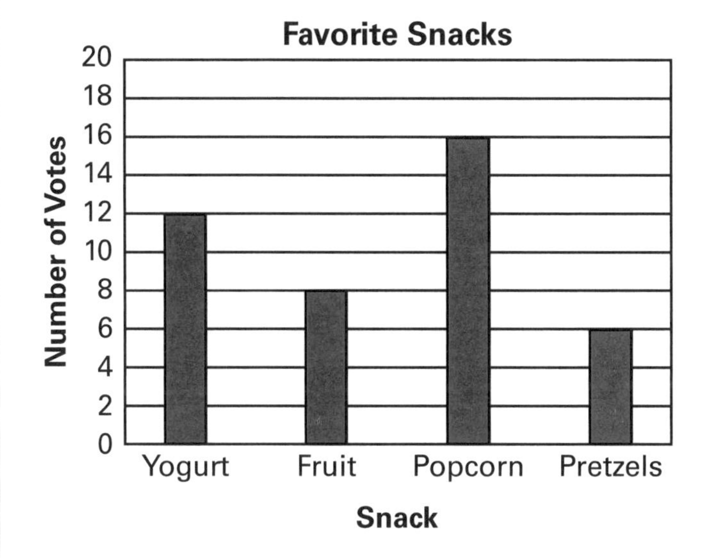

5. Which snack got the fewest number of votes?

   Ⓐ yogurt
   Ⓑ fruit
   Ⓒ popcorn
   Ⓓ pretzels

6. How many fewer votes did fruit get than yogurt?

   Ⓐ 2
   Ⓑ 4
   Ⓒ 6
   Ⓓ 8

Study the model. It is a good example of a written answer.

Student Model

Show

The bar graph shows the number of sports cards Sally has.

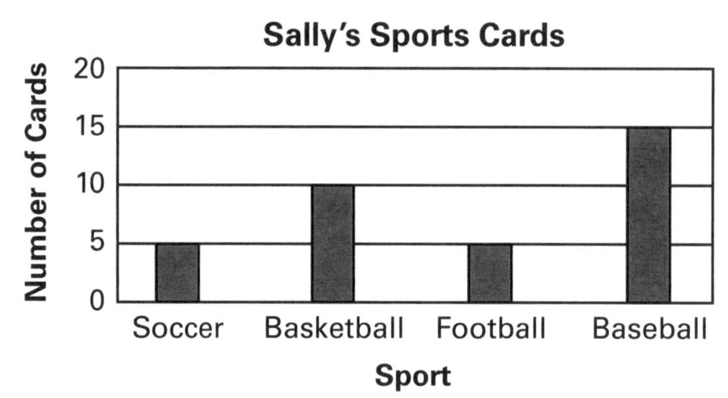

How many more baseball cards than soccer cards does Sally have?

Use pictures, words, or numbers to show your work.

15 baseball cards

5 soccer cards

15 − 5 = 10

Solution: Sally has <u>10</u> more baseball cards than soccer cards.

☑ The student shows each step.

☑ The student correctly answers the question asked.

Explain

Explain how you got your answer.

I followed the top of the bar for baseball cards to the scale on the left. I read 15. Then I followed the top of the bar for soccer cards to the scale. I read 5. I subtracted 15 − 5 to compare the data. Sally has 10 more baseball cards than soccer cards.

☑ The student gives important details about how to find the difference in cards.

☑ The student uses the math words *scale*, *subtract*, and *data*.

Your Turn **Solve the problem. Use what you learned from the model.**

CHECKLIST

Did you . . .

- ☐ show each step?
- ☐ answer the question asked?
- ☐ give important details?
- ☐ use math words?

7. The bar graph shows the colors of cars in a parking lot.

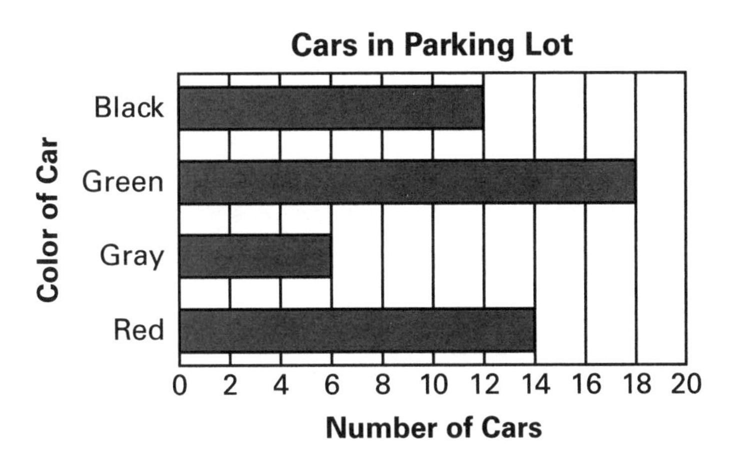

How many more black cars than gray cars are in the parking lot?

Use pictures, words, or numbers to show your work.

Solution: There are _______ more black cars than gray cars.

Explain how you got your answer.

____

____

____

____

____

PART **FIVE:** Prepare for a Test

As you read graphs, remember to
- use the key on a pictograph to find how many each picture stands for.
- follow the top or end of bars on bar graphs to the scale.
- pay close attention to the scale. Do the numbers increase by 1, by 2, by 5?

Solve each problem.

Use the pictograph for problems 8 and 9.

The pictograph shows the favorite colors of third-grade students.

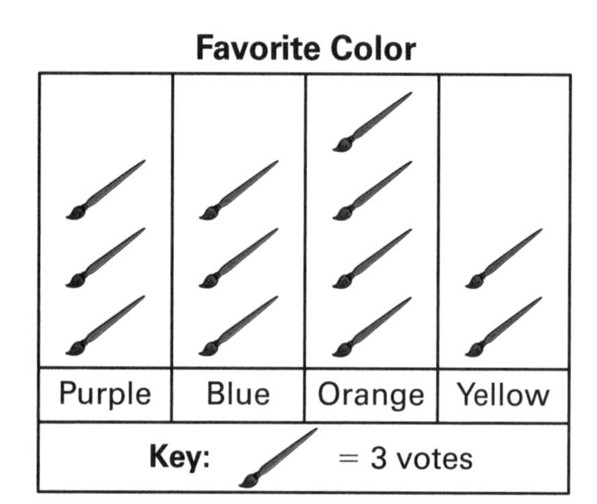

8. How many students voted for blue?

Ⓐ 3 Ⓑ 6 Ⓒ 9 Ⓓ 12

9. How many fewer students voted for yellow than purple?

Ⓐ 0 Ⓑ 1 Ⓒ 3 Ⓓ 8

Use the bar graph for problems 10 and 11.

The bar graph shows the number of trash items that a class collected at a park.

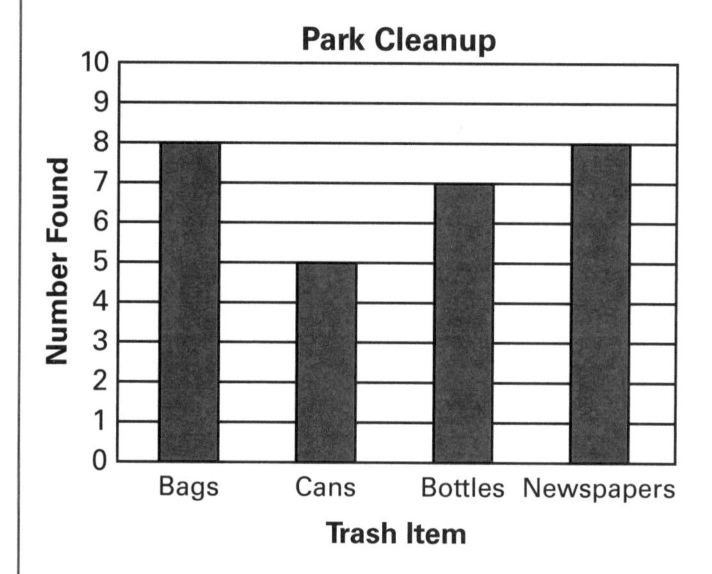

10. How many cans did students find?

Ⓐ 4 Ⓑ 5 Ⓒ 6 Ⓓ 7

11. How many more bags than bottles did students find?

Ⓐ 1 Ⓑ 2 Ⓒ 3 Ⓓ 4

Use the pictograph for problems 12 and 13.

The pictograph shows how many students bought T-shirts in each size.

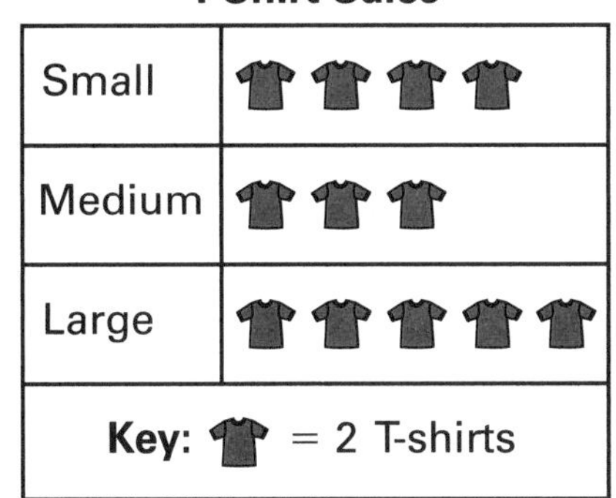

12. How many T-shirts were bought in all?

    Ⓐ 12 Ⓑ 20 Ⓒ 24 Ⓓ 26

13. How many more small T-shirts than medium T-shirts did students buy?

    Ⓐ 1 Ⓑ 2 Ⓒ 4 Ⓓ 6

14. The bar graph shows how many frozen yogurt bars students bought in different flavors.

Did students buy more strawberry yogurt bars or banana yogurt bars? How many more?

Students bought ______ more

______________ bars

than ______________ bars.

15. The pictograph shows the colors of party balloons. How many more blue and green balloons are there than yellow balloons?

    Use pictures, words, or numbers to show your work.

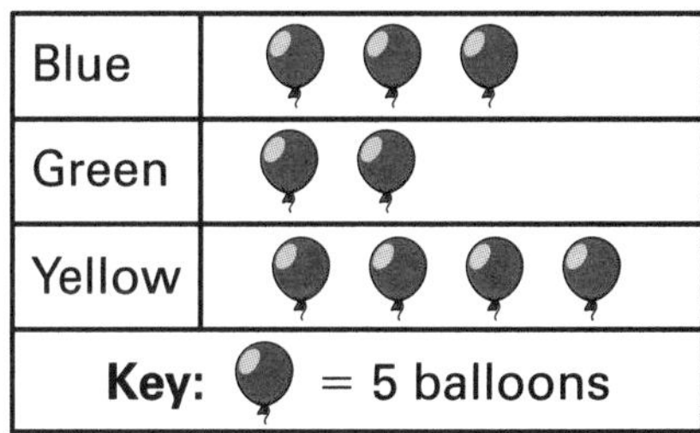

Solution: ______ more blue and green balloons

Explain how you found your answer.

____

____

____

Additional Lesson

Lesson 17 UNDERSTAND AREA

PART ONE: Learn About Area

How can you measure the inside of a figure?

Explore

The distance around a figure is the **perimeter**. To find the perimeter of any figure, you add the lengths of all its sides.

Perimeter = 3 + 3 + 2 + 2 + 1 + 1 = 12

The perimeter of this figure is 12 units.

How can you measure the inside of a figure?

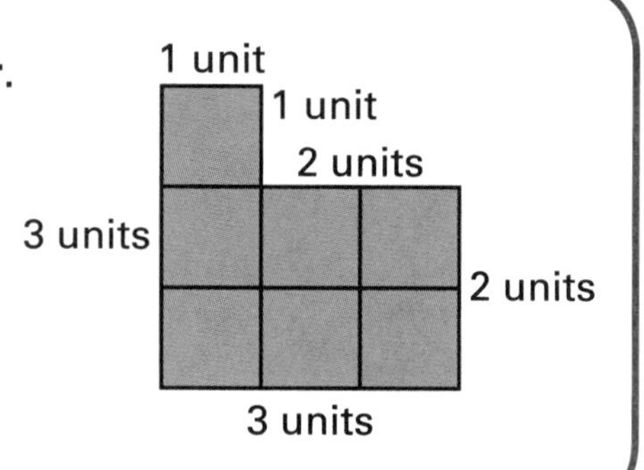

Think

This square shows a **square unit**.

A square unit is __1__ unit wide and __1__ unit long.

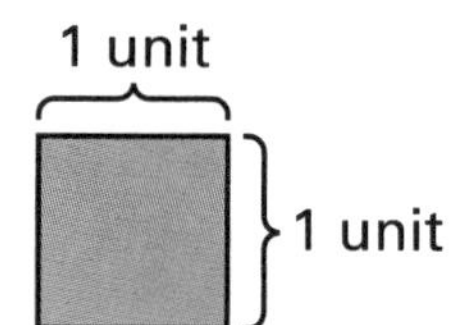

Connect

You use square units to measure **area**.
Area is the number of square units inside a figure.

To measure the area of a figure, you count the number of square units that are in the figure.

There are 8 square units in this figure.
So, the area is 8 square units.

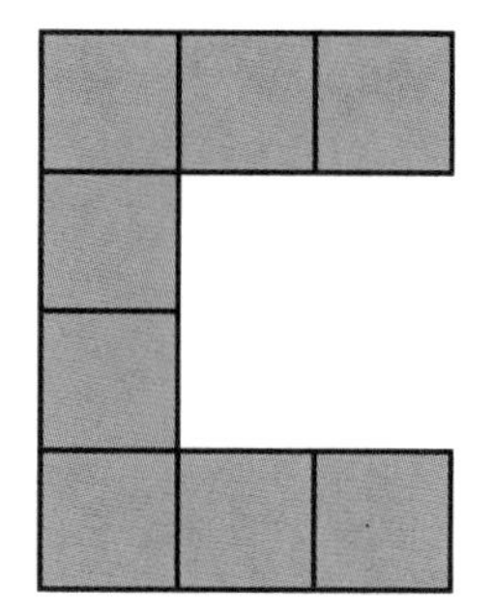

Let's Talk

Suppose each square unit in the figure in **Connect** was 1 inch long and 1 inch wide. What would be the area of the figure?

Fill in the blanks. Solve the problem.

Rex's dad is using square tiles to design a kitchen floor. The design is shown below. Each tile is 1 square foot. What is the area of the floor?

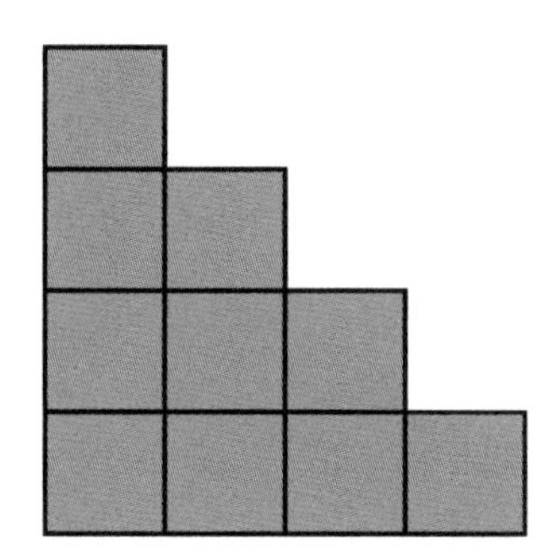

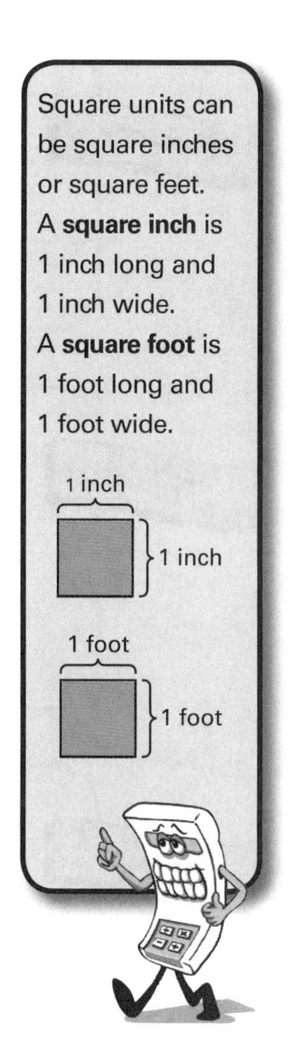

- Count the square units in the figure.
- There are _____ square units in the figure.

  Each square unit is 1 square __________.

  There are _____ square feet in the figure.

Solution: The area of the floor is _____ square feet.

Now, use what you know to solve this problem.

1. Find the area of the figure.

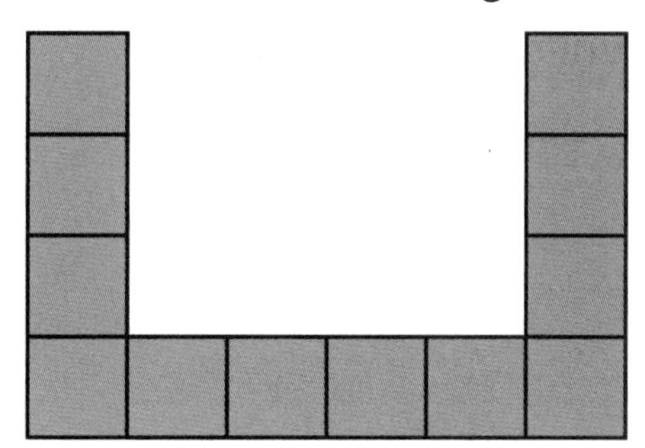

Ⓐ 10 square units

Ⓑ 12 square units

Ⓒ 14 square units

Ⓓ 26 square units

How can you find the area of different kinds of figures?

Explore

Area is the number of square units inside a figure.

The area of this figure is 9 square units.

How do you find the area of a figure that has some square units that are whole and some that are not?

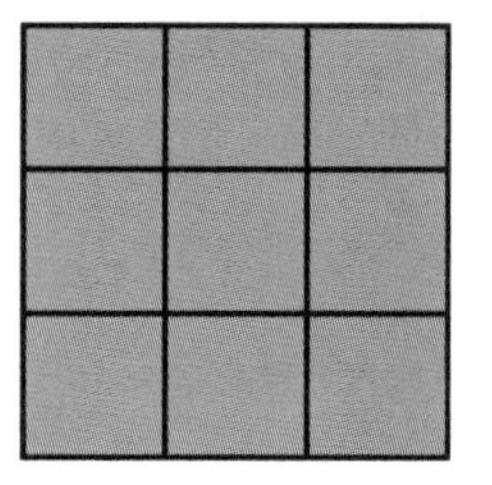

Think

How many whole square units are in this figure? 9

How many half square units are in this figure? 6

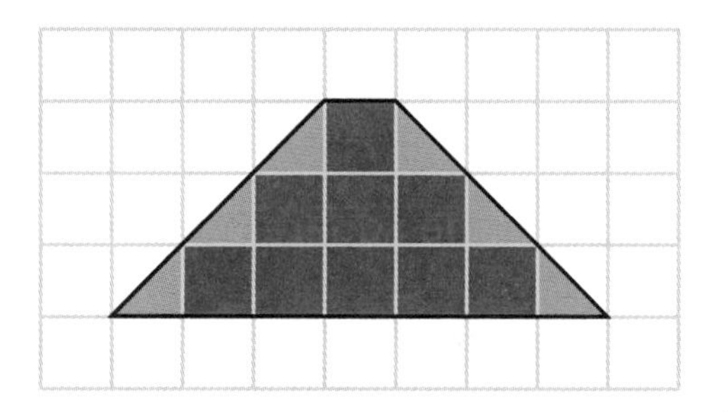

Connect

To find the area of the figure:

1. Find how many whole units the half units make.

   2 half square units = 1 whole square unit,
   so 6 half square units = 3 whole square units

2. Add to find the total number of whole square units.

   9 + 3 = 12 square units

The area of the figure is 12 square units.

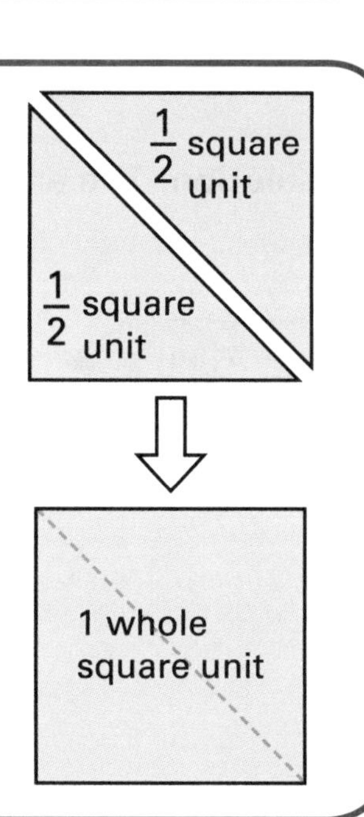

Let's Talk

Suppose the figure in **Think** was drawn on grid paper with squares that are 1 centimeter long and 1 centimeter wide. What would be the area of the figure? Explain how you got your answer.

Fill in the blanks. Solve the problem.

Jeff cut fabric in the shape of the figure below.
Each square unit is a square centimeter.

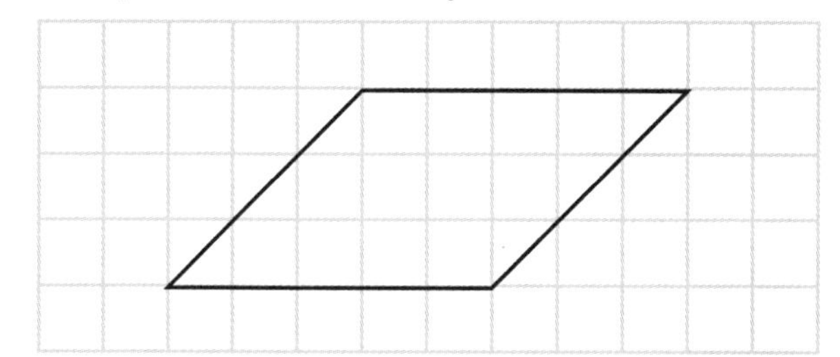

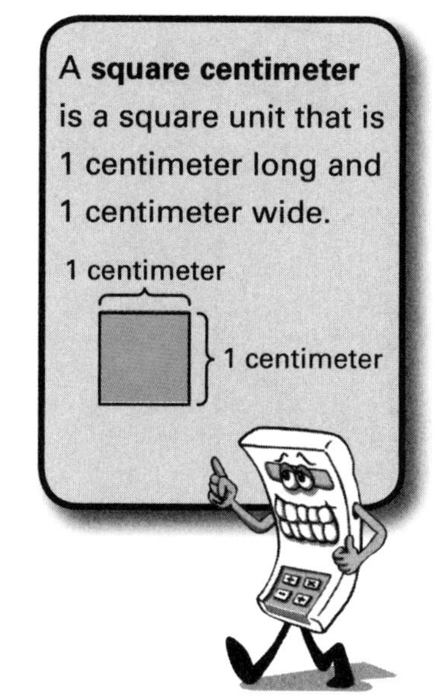

What is the area of the fabric Jeff cut?

- Shade the number of whole square units one color.

  There are _____ whole square units.

- Shade the number of half square units another color.

  There are _____ half square units.

  This is the same as _____ whole square units.

- Add to find the total number of whole square units.

  _____ + _____ = _____ square units

- Each square unit is a ______________________________.

Solution: The area of the fabric is _____ square centimeters.

Now, use what you know to solve this problem.

2. Find the area of the figure.

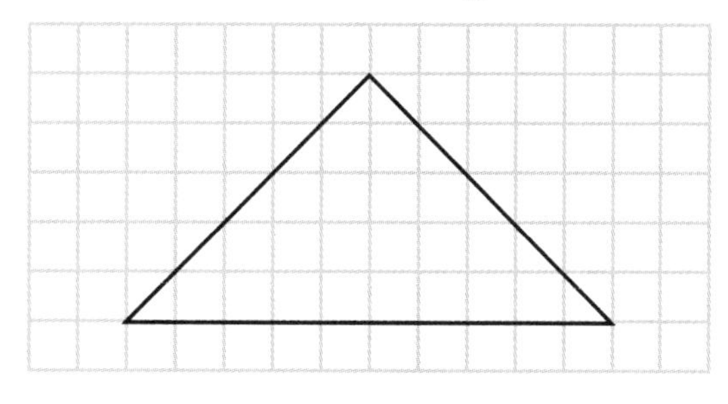

_____ square units

Solve the problem. Then read why each answer choice is correct or not correct.

Solve

Jermaine drew the design below on grid paper that has 1-inch by 1-inch squares.

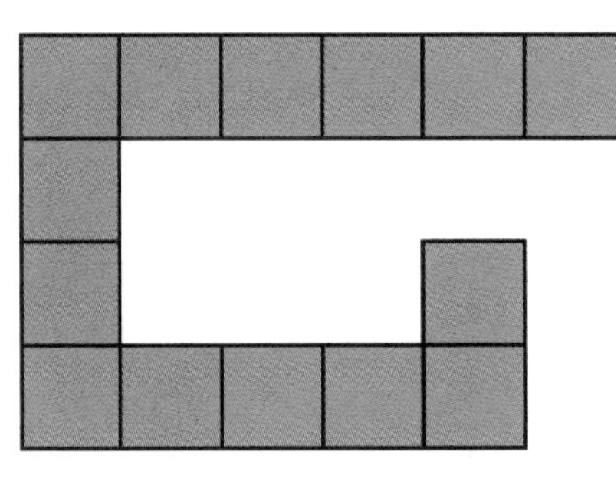

What is the area of the design?

Ⓐ 30 square inches
Ⓑ 14 square inches
Ⓒ 12 square inches
Ⓓ 11 square inches

Check

Check to see if you chose the correct answer.

To find the area, count the square units.
There are 14 square units in the design.
Each square is a square inch.

So, the correct answer is Ⓑ.

Why are the other answer choices not correct?

Ⓐ 30 square inches	This is the perimeter, or distance around the outside, of the figure.
Ⓒ 12 square inches	Not all of the square units in the figure have been counted.
Ⓓ 11 square inches	This is the area of the top and bottom of the figure, not the entire figure.

Your Turn **Solve each problem. Use the hints to avoid mistakes.**

- Mark each square unit with a dot as you count it so you do not count it twice.
- Decide if the figure has half square units. Count 2 half square units as 1 square unit.

3. Each square is 1 square inch. What is the area of the figure?

Ⓐ 5 square inches

Ⓑ 9 square inches

Ⓒ 10 square inches

Ⓓ 20 square inches

4. What is the area of the figure?

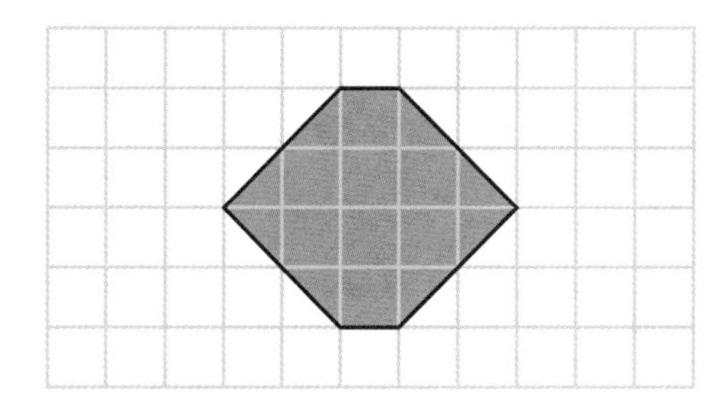

Ⓐ 8 square units

Ⓑ 10 square units

Ⓒ 12 square units

Ⓓ 16 square units

5. What is the area of the figure?

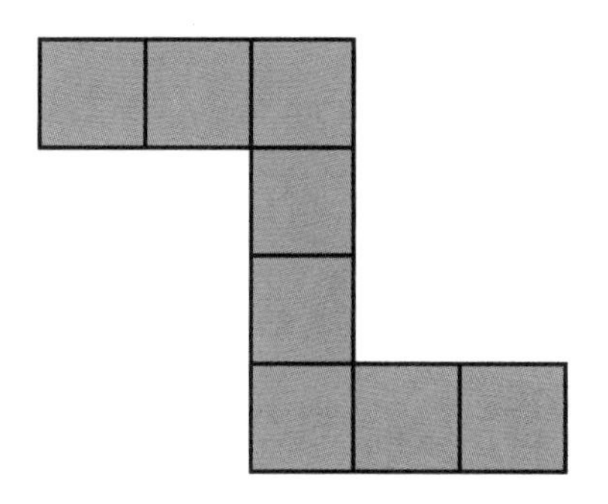

Ⓐ 8 square units

Ⓑ 9 square units

Ⓒ 10 square units

Ⓓ 18 square units

6. Each square is a square foot. What is the area of the figure?

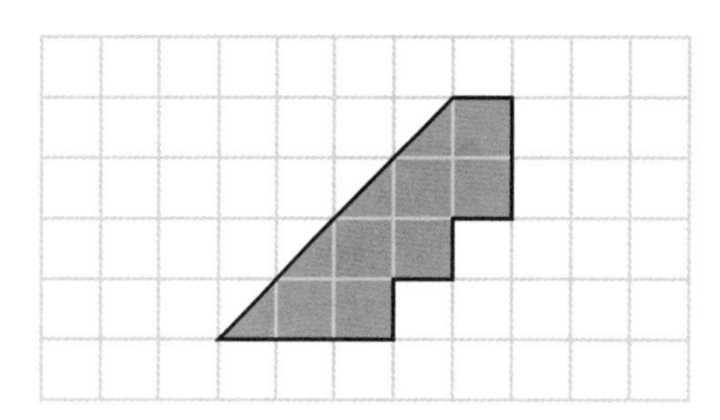

Ⓐ 7 square feet

Ⓑ 9 square feet

Ⓒ 11 square feet

Ⓓ 14 square feet

Study the model. It is a good example of a written answer.

Student Model

Show

Mr. Hernandes put a carpet shaped like the figure below in his classroom. Each square is 1 square meter. What is the area of the carpet?

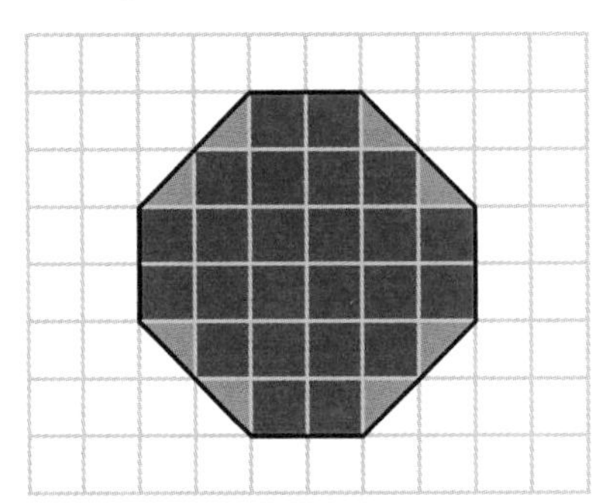

Use pictures, words, or numbers to show your work.

whole square units: 24
half square units: 8 = 4 whole square units
24 + 4 = 28 square units

Solution: 28 square meters

Explain

Explain how you got your answer.

First, I counted the number of whole square units. There are 24. Then I counted the half square units. There are 8. I combined them to make 4 whole square units. Then I added to find the total number of whole square units: 24 + 4 = 28. Each square is 1 square meter, so the area is 28 square meters.

☑ The student shows each step.

☑ The student correctly answers the question asked.

☑ The student gives important details about how to find the area.

☑ The student uses the math words *square units, half square units, square meter,* and *area.*

Your Turn **Solve the problem. Use what you learned from the model.**

7. Don is making the banner shown. Each square is 1 square inch. What is the area of Don's banner?

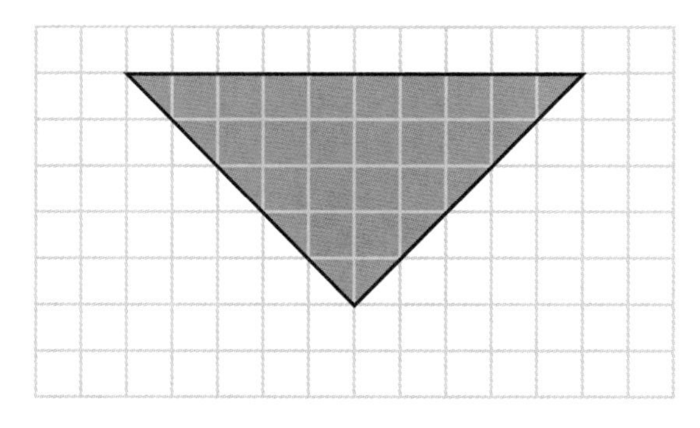

Use pictures, words, or numbers to show your work.

Solution: _____ square inches

Explain how you got your answer.

____

____

____

____

____

CHECKLIST

Did you . . .

- ☐ show each step?
- ☐ answer the question asked?
- ☐ give important details?
- ☐ use math words?

As you solve area problems, remember to:
- count whole square units *and* half square units.
- combine 2 half square units to make 1 whole square unit.
- check if the square unit has a certain measurement.

Solve each problem.

8. Kashia's mom used this pattern for their new patio. Each square is 1 square foot. What is the area of the patio?

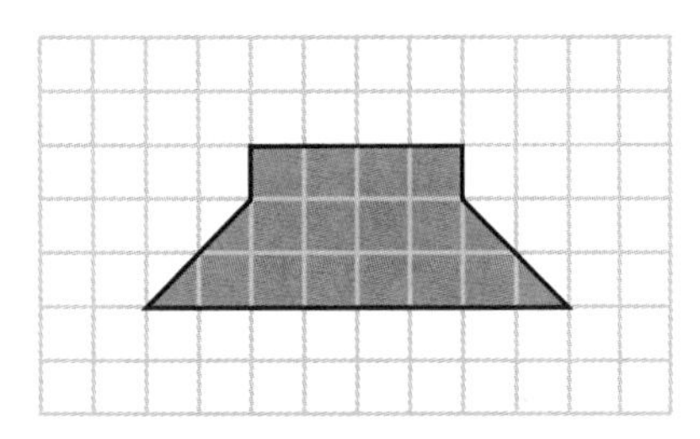

Ⓐ 14 square feet

Ⓑ 15 square feet

Ⓒ 16 square feet

Ⓓ 18 square feet

9. What is the area of the figure?

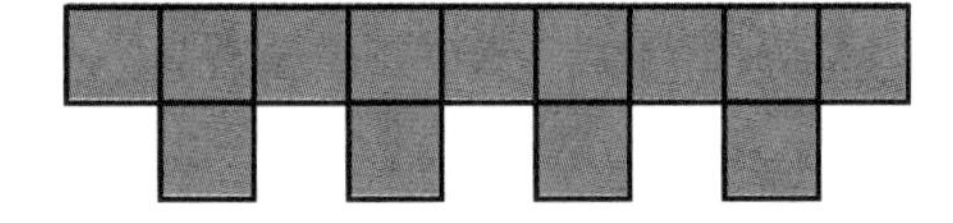

Ⓐ 13 square units

Ⓑ 18 square units

Ⓒ 24 square units

Ⓓ 28 square units

10. What is the area of the figure?

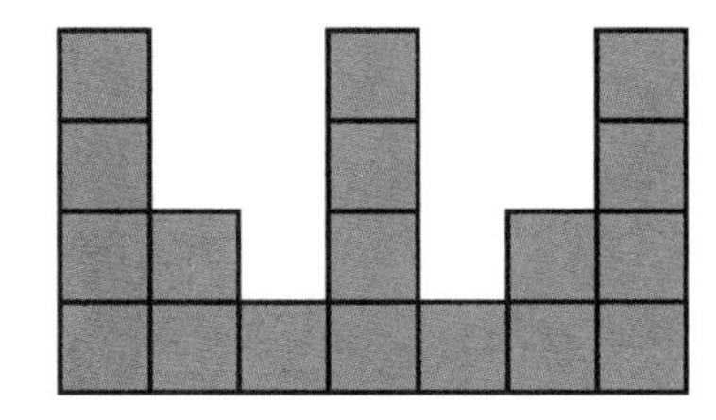

Ⓐ 34 square units

Ⓑ 28 square units

Ⓒ 20 square units

Ⓓ 18 square units

11. Wang is painting the design below on the wall of his room. Each square is 1 square foot. What is the area of the design?

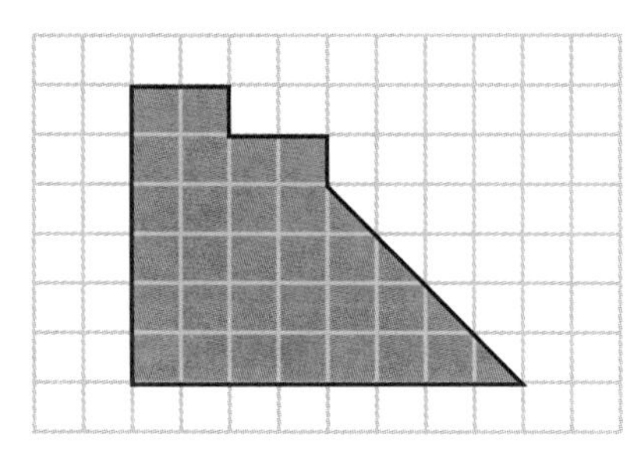

Ⓐ 24 square feet

Ⓑ 28 square feet

Ⓒ 30 square feet

Ⓓ 32 square feet

12. What is the area of the figure?

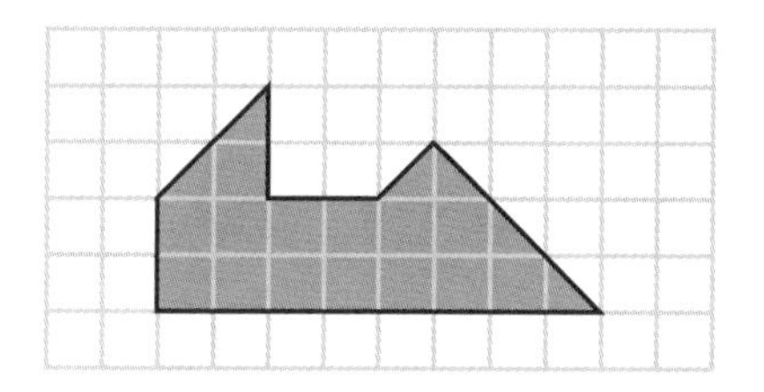

Ⓐ 17 square units Ⓒ 19 square units
Ⓑ 18 square units Ⓓ 20 square units

13. Mr. Brown painted the pattern below on the floor of the school's music room. Each square is 1 square foot. What is the area of the pattern?

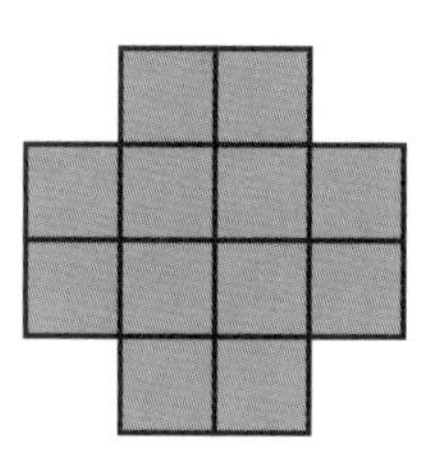

Ⓐ 8 square feet Ⓒ 16 square feet
Ⓑ 12 square feet Ⓓ 20 square feet

14. Ramani drew the design below. Each square is 1 square inch. What is the area of Ramani's design?

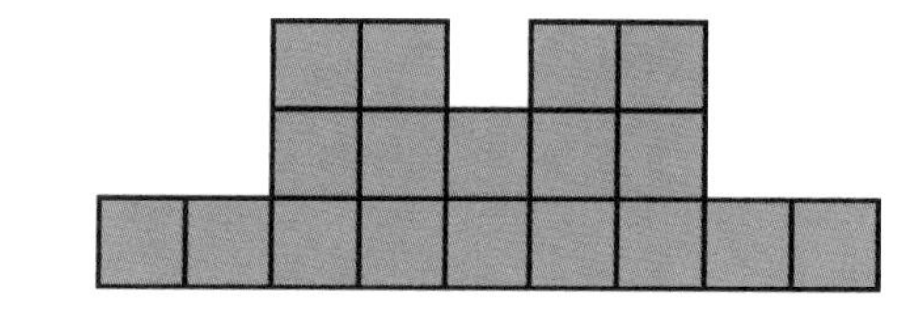

_____ square inches

15. The figure shown is a design on a blanket. Each square of the design is 1 square inch. What is the area of the design?

Use pictures, words, or numbers to show your work.

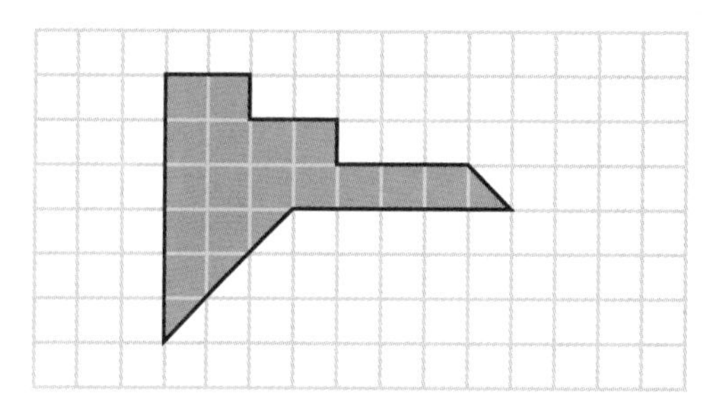

Solution: _____ square inches

Explain how you got your answer.

____

____

____

____